HEALTHY COOK'S

ANTI INFLAMMATORY

DIET & COOKBOOK

OVER 100 SCIENCE-BASED SUPERFOOD MEALS FOR IMPROVED GUT HEALTH, STRESS REDUCTION & DETOXIFICATION

Albert Orbinati, Ph.D.

THIS BOOK IS DEDICATED TO MY MOTHER, FREDA, WHOSE TABBOULEH IS SECOND TO NONE, AND WHO TAUGHT ME (AMONG MANY THINGS IN LIFE) THE VALUE OF COOKING WITH FRESH AND CLEAN INGREDIENTS.

I LOVE YOU, MOM.

أنا أحب كي اي أمي

TABLE OF CONTENTS

INTRODUCTION

Welcome to a journey of transformation and wellness through the power of food. This cookbook is designed not just as a collection of recipes, but as a down-to-earth, honest, and comprehensive guide to understanding and implementing an anti-inflammatory diet that promotes better health and vitality. Whether you're looking to alleviate chronic inflammation, manage pain, or simply improve your overall well-being, the meals you'll discover here are crafted to enrich your body with nutrients that heal and restore.

I focused on writing this book in an honest way. Most of the anti-inflammatory cookbooks you can purchase on Amazon (and elsewhere) promise simplicity, low cost, and easy life implementation. And, unfortunately, many are selling snake oil. For example, while the recipes may be easy to make (most are very simple) from my personal experience, an anti-inflammatory diet is not inexpensive, despite what is promised to you on the cover of a book. The main ingredients you should stock your shelves with do not necessarily come cheap. I needed to make small adjustments to my lifestyle in order to afford a regular anti-inflammatory diet. Most books will not tell you this. That's the honest truth.

If you're able to make these commitments, then congratulations! A world of health awaits you! An anti-inflammatory diet focuses on whole, nutrient-dense foods that are rich in antioxidants, healthy fats, and phytonutrients which help mitigate the adverse effects of chronic inflammation. What you'll find in the pages to come are recipes that use powerful anti-inflammatory ingredients (I call them "anti-inflammatories") and other beneficial nutrients that help to supercharge healing.

Each recipe in this book is carefully formulated not only to deliver maximum flavor but also to ensure that every meal brings you a step closer to a healthier life. And nearly each recipe is designed to be flexible. For protein, there are vegan, vegetarian, and meat options available. If you don't like a protein option, you can easily swap it out for another. Why? Because the *proteins are not the star of the show*. The other beneficial ingredients are. Don't like tofu? Use free range chicken. Don't care for turkey? Use beans instead. Turmeric have you running for the hills? Well...that one is a bit more difficult. We like turmeric in this book.

Whether you are new to the concept of an anti-inflammatory diet or are looking to expand your repertoire of health-supporting recipes, I hope you enjoy my honest process of discovering how simple, enjoyable, and satisfying it can be to care for your body through mindful nutrition! *-AO*

WHAT IS INFLAMMATION?

Inflammation is the body's natural response to protect itself against harm. If you've sprained your ankle, you know what inflammation looks and feels like. This is called acute inflammation. It's short term, natural, and there for your own good.

However, there is also internal inflammation that you cannot necessarily see or feel. It affects your arteries and tissues. It grows over time through chronic stress, poor eating habits, lack of exercise, and genetic conditions. When this internal inflammation becomes chronic, it can lead to numerous health issues, including arthritis, heart disease, IBS, and various other autoimmune conditions. This was the case for me. I needed to take back control of my health.

Enter: the anti-inflammatory diet, which really should be called the anti-inflammation *lifestyle* given that there's more you need to do, in addition to diet, to control your inflammation.

CHAPTER 1:
ADAPTING TO THE ANTI-INFLAMMATORY LIFESTYLE

I can tell you from first-hand experience that adjusting to and adopting an anti-inflammatory diet is just one step in what will, inevitably, need to become a *lifestyle* if you're serious about inflammation. Diet is important, and perhaps the most important, but it's not the only change you'll need to make. Becoming intentional about your approach to reducing inflammation, and taking steps like engaging in regular exercise, drinking plenty of water each day, and taking time to relax, in combination with diet, are choices that produce real results. I won't get into details about those because, well, this is a cookbook. But know that you will have to exercise regularly, drink water, and take steps to relax and meditate. This formula is the lifestyle that you will need to adapt.

There are also other intentional (incredibly useful) steps you can take. **First, make an appointment with your doctor and have conversations about your inflammation. Order an allergy test and blood test to get an indication of your food intolerances. There may be foods you are allergic to but don't feel the immediate effects of.** This was the case for me.

You might also try keeping a food diary, considering elimination diets for a certain amount of time, in addition to your food intolerances. Let's look at each of these recommendations in more detail.

SEEK EXPERT ADVICE
Before following the recipes in this book, **I strongly encourage you to meet with your doctor, or a registered dietitian *first*.** Consulting a healthcare professional before starting an anti-inflammatory diet is important for several reasons:

Individual Need
We all have different health conditions, dietary preferences, and nutritional needs. A healthcare professional can provide a diet plan tailored to your specific requirements. The recommendations in this book are just that – *recommendations* – and you should follow them while also following your specific dietary needs. The good news? All of the recipes are flexible. For example, you can swap out proteins to something that better suits your conditions and preferences. For example, if you can't eat nightshades (tomatoes, peppers, eggplants, etc.), remove them from the recipe or try another recipe. You can also easily control sugars in the sweeter recipes.

Existing Conditions

Consult a healthcare professional because chronic conditions are challenging to control. Chronic conditions like diabetes, kidney disease, or digestive issues often require specific dietary modifications, in addition to medications, that only a medical expert can adequately address and prescribe. Through these tests, you'll learn about your food intolerances.

Nutrient-Drug Interaction

Consult a healthcare professional because some foods can interact with medications, altering their effectiveness or causing adverse reactions. For example, certain anti-inflammatory foods might affect blood thinning medications.

Supplement Guidance

Consult a healthcare professional because only a doctor can ensure that supplements are safe and appropriate given your current medications. I make no suplement recommendations in this book.

Deficiency Risk

Consult a healthcare professional because any planned diet may inadvertently lead to nutrient deficiencies if not properly monitored. Professional guidance ensures balanced nutrition. You may also want to seek out a registered nutritionist in your area.

Accurate Diagnosis

Consult a healthcare professional because the symptoms that motivate someone to adopt an anti-inflammatory diet (like pain, swelling, fatigue) may have different underlying causes that require specific treatment beyond diet.

Lab Tests and Monitoring

Consult a healthcare professional because they can conduct appropriate tests to identify inflammation levels and monitor progress over time. Allergy and blood tests are the most common.

Safe Foods

Consult a healthcare professional because some anti-inflammatory foods, like nuts or certain spices, can trigger allergies or sensitivities. Allergy testing can prevent adverse reactions.

Lifestyle Integration

Finally, consult a healthcare professional because an anti-inflammatory diet is often more effective when combined with other lifestyle changes like exercise or stress reduction. Medical experts can provide you with a comprehensive plan.

KEEP A FOOD DIARY

I cannot stress this enough: **Take detailed notes on everything you eat and any symptoms you experience.** Take notes on the time, types of food eaten, portion sizes, and any physical or mental symptoms that occur after eating. If you experience any reactions, rate them from 1 to 10 and take note of any accompanying symptoms. Food journaling is one of the only ways to understand how your diet is affecting your well-being. **The issue is that most of us don't bother to intentionally monitor our bodily reactions.** I certainly didn't...until I did. Food diaries describe the details about your food, any reactions, and any hints about daily meal prep. This diary will also come in very handy when you meet with your healthcare professional.

TRY AN ELIMINATION DIET

An elimination diet can be followed with expert supervision. This involves removing certain foods or food categories from the diet for a set period, often two to six weeks, and then gradually reintroducing them to detect any adverse reactions. An elimination diet can also help you focus on foods that cause inflammation or discomfort.

Elimination diets have been used for decades by allergists and nutritionists to find the root cause of a reaction, target inflammatory responses, and control blood sugar. An example of an elimination diet is the **two-week sugar detox** where you eliminate sugar for about three-or-so days, and for the rest of the two weeks, limit your sugar (and carbohydrate) intake. I've done this elimination method a few times and can tell you, directly, that it worked wonders for my body and brain. Consult with your doctor first, and then try it out for yourself – there are plenty of YouTube videos that can walk you through it.

Do keep in mind that during an elimination diet, you'll initially experience symptoms like bloating, fatigue, headaches, insomnia, or joint pain, among others. These symptoms can be experienced for up to two to three days once the elimination diet has started and could continue until the offending food has been removed from your body. Take note of your symptoms and write them in your food diary. Elimination diets follow a trial-and-error format, and in time, you will learn what triggers to watch out for and what food to avoid.

UNDERSTAND THE ROLE OF MACRONUTRIENTS

In an anti-inflammatory diet, macronutrients—proteins, carbohydrates, and fats—play distinct roles in fighting inflammation and promoting overall health.

Proteins

Proteins are essential for building and repairing tissues, particularly through collagen production, which is crucial for joint health. Certain amino acids, such as glutamine and arginine, help maintain gut integrity and modulate the immune system. Lean protein sources like fatty fish provide omega-3 fatty acids (EPA and DHA), which have potent anti-inflammatory effects, while plant-based proteins offer fiber and antioxidants. I tried my best to develop recipes that would reduce pro-inflammatory protein sources like pork and red meat. You'll see a lot of beans, legumes, tofu, seafood, and limited recipes with chicken and turkey.

Carbohydrates

Carbs serve as an important energy source, especially complex carbohydrates that provide sustained energy and prevent blood sugar spikes, which can trigger inflammation. Dietary fiber from these carbohydrates also promotes gut health by fostering a diverse microbiome that produces anti-inflammatory short-chain fatty acids like butyrate. Complex carbohydrates are generally higher in fiber as well. High-fiber diets have been associated with lower levels of C-reactive protein (CRP), a marker of inflammation. Whole grains are rich in antioxidants such as selenium and zinc, while fruits and vegetables contain vitamins, flavonoids, and polyphenols that help neutralize free radicals.

Balance and moderation is the key with complex carbs. You don't want to over-do it because, well, carbs are carbs. If you consume them and don't use them right away, they'll turn into glucose in your body and will eventually be stored as fat. Moderation is the name of the game, combined with regular exercise.

Fats

Fats, particularly essential fatty acids, also have a crucial role in regulating inflammation. **Omega-3 fatty acids** from fish oil and plant sources reduce pro-inflammatory eicosanoids, which are lipids associated with various inflammatory diseases, including cancer.

According to the American Heart Association, **monounsaturated fats**, like those found in olive oil, avocados, and nuts, "help reduce bad cholesterol levels in your blood, which can lower your risk of heart disease and stroke. They also provide nutrients to help develop and maintain your body's cells. Oils rich in monounsaturated fats also provide vitamin E, an important antioxidant."

Polyunsaturated fats in nuts and seeds provide a balanced ratio of omega-3 and omega-6 fatty acids, which is essential for controlling inflammation. According to MedlinePlus, **Omega-3 fatty acids** are good for your heart in several ways. They help:

1. Reduce triglycerides, a type of fat in your blood
2. Reduce the risk of developing an irregular heartbeat (arrhythmia)
3. Slow the buildup of plaque, a substance comprising fat, cholesterol, and calcium, which can harden and clog your arteries
4. Slightly lower your blood pressure

Omega-6 fatty acids may help to:

1. Control your blood sugar
2. Reduce your risk for diabetes
3. Lower your blood pressure

Several vitamins and minerals have anti-inflammatory properties and can help reduce inflammation when included as part of a balanced diet. Here's a list of key vitamins and minerals known for their anti-inflammatory effects:

VITAMINS	SOURCES	ANTI-INFLAMMATORY ROLE
D	Sunlight, fortified foods, fatty fish, egg yolks	Helps modulate the immune system, reducing pro-inflammatory cytokines. Low levels are associated with increased inflammation.
C	Citrus fruits, strawberries, bell peppers, broccoli.	An antioxidant that reduces oxidative stress and inflammatory markers like CRP (C-reactive protein).
E	Nuts, seeds, spinach, avocado.	A potent antioxidant that neutralizes free radicals and inhibits pro-inflammatory enzymes.
A (Retinoids & Carotenoids)	Liver, carrots, sweet potatoes, leafy greens.	Carotenoids like beta-carotene reduce oxidative stress, while retinoids modulate immune function.
K	Leafy greens, broccoli, Brussels sprouts.	Reduces inflammatory markers, particularly in conditions like rheumatoid arthritis.
B Vitamins (B6, B9 & B12)	B6: Poultry, fish, bananas, chickpeas; B9 (Folate): Leafy greens, legumes; B12: fortified plant-based foods.	Reduce homocysteine levels, which are linked to inflammation. B6 also plays a role in cytokine regulation.

MINERALS	SOURCES	ANTI-INFLAMMATORY ROLE
Magnesium	Nuts, seeds, leafy greens, whole grains.	Reduces CRP levels and regulates cytokines, thus reducing inflammation.
Zinc	Seafood, meat, seeds, legumes.	Modulates immune response and reduces oxidative stress and inflammatory cytokines.
Selenium	Brazil nuts, seafood, eggs, whole grains.	Antioxidant that reduces oxidative stress and lowers CRP levels.
Copper	Shellfish, nuts, seeds, whole grains.	Supports antioxidant enzyme function, thus reducing inflammation.
Iron	Red meat, poultry, fish, legumes, leafy greens.	Essential for immune function. Anemia (iron deficiency) can exacerbate inflammation.
Potassium	Bananas, avocados, leafy greens, potatoes.	Helps regulate blood pressure and reduces CRP levels.
Calcium	Dairy products, leafy greens, fortified plant-based milks.	Modulates the immune system and reduces the risk of inflammatory conditions like osteoporosis.

CHAPTER 2:
ESSENTIAL ANTI-INFLAMMATORY INGREDIENTS

An anti-inflammatory diet not only can reduce your chronic inflammation, but also help you lose weight, improve brain health, clear skin conditions, and much more. And, in combination, many nutrients have **multiplier effects** which boost their beneficial properties and can help with issues like nutrient absorption.

For example, turmeric, the primary spice utilized in curry, possesses potent anti-inflammatory properties, and contributes to the regulation of blood sugar, digestion, and even the suppression of cancer growth. Sadly, curcuminoids, which are the active anti-inflammatory component of turmeric, have a low absorption rate when consumed by themselves. By using a small amount of black pepper, you can enhance the absorption of curcuminoids by an average of 2000% and thereby fully optimize the potent advantages of this nutrient combination.

WHAT TO STOCK YOUR PANTRY WITH

You'll see these foods and ingredients repeated many times in this cookbook. My recommendation is to stock your pantry and refrigerator with them. I will say, however, many do not come cheap. It's an unfortunate reality of the anti-inflammatory diet, and a reality I completely empathize with. My recommendation is to do your best. It's okay if you can't have everything in your pantry. Stick to the foundational ingredients, which I've labeled for you. Stock what you can and make sure you're getting plenty of exercise and reducing your overall sugar intake, both of which make a *huge* difference.

Healthy Oils and Fats

- **Extra Virgin Olive Oil (foundational):** A staple in many recipes in this book, rich in monounsaturated fats and antioxidants. I recommend single origin, cold pressed olive oils for the best flavor. They're more expensive than non-single origin olive oils.
- **Avocado Oil:** Another super healthy fat source that's used in various recipes, especially for higher-heat cooking (which olive oil is not). Unfortunately, avocado oil can get pricey. Olive oil is more cost effective and has similar health benefits.

Nuts and Seeds

- **Almonds (foundational):** Used in both sweet and savory dishes, almonds provide vitamin E and healthy fats. Most almond packages are reasonably priced.
- **Flaxseeds:** Rich in omega-3 fatty acids, flaxseeds are used in many of my recipes. A bag of flax goes a long way.
- **Chia Seeds:** Found in smoothies and puddings, they are high in fiber and omega-3s. Same as flax, a bag of chia goes a long way.

Whole Grains

- **Oats:** Oats contain 24 phenolic compounds, which are plant compounds that have antioxidant properties. One of these groups, avenanthramides, are almost exclusively found in oats and can help reduce inflammation. I strongly suggest a company like Bob's Red Mill, which does not use nasty chemicals to process their oats. It's more expensive, but worth it to avoid the chemicals.
- **Quinoa (foundational):** A versatile grain, quinoa is used in salads and main dishes, providing protein and fiber. While pricey, a container of quinoa goes a long way.

Spices and Herbs

- **Turmeric (foundational):** A powerhouse anti-inflammatory spice found in many of my recipes, especially in scrambles and stews. As of this writing, My advice is to visit your local health food retailer, or go to Amazon and buy turmeric by the pound, which drastically reduces the long term costs of this power spice.
- **Cinnamon (foundational):** Used in both breakfast and dessert recipes, cinnamon is known for its anti-inflammatory properties and can be found inexpensively. Woohoo!
- **Cumin (foundational):** Often paired with turmeric, cumin is a key spice in many savory dishes, and can also be found inexpensively.
- **Garlic Powder and Fresh Garlic (foundational):** A staple in my recipes, offering a rich source of allicin, which is known for its anti-inflammatory effects. Great news - garlic is plentiful and cheap.
- **Black Pepper (foundational):** Often used to enhance the absorption of turmeric, black pepper is essential in your pantry. It's also one of the cheapest spieces you can buy!

Legumes

- **Chickpeas (foundational):** Frequently used in my salads and stews, chickpeas are a great source of protein and fiber. They're also affordable!
- **Lentils:** Found in many of my soups and stews, lentils provide protein, fiber, and a range of micronutrients. They also are inexpensive.

Vegetables

- **Sweet Potatoes (foundational):** A common ingredient in both breakfast and dinner recipes, sweet potatoes are rich in beta-carotene and vitamin C. And good news! Sweet potatoes (unlike regular potatoes) are not nightshades, which many people have trouble digesting. Sweet potatoes are part of the morning glory family of plants.
- **Kale and Spinach (foundational):** These leafy greens are used across most of my dishes, from smoothies to salads, offering vitamins A, C, K, and antioxidants. They're also inexpensive!

- **Bell Peppers:** Often used in my hashes and salads, bell peppers are packed with vitamin C and antioxidants. Keep in mind, however, that peppers are nightshades. You may have trouble digesting them. This is why you should get tested for food allergies and sensitivites before using this book.

Fruits

- **Berries (Blue, Black, Rasp, Straw; foundational):** Commonly used in my breakfast recipes, they are super high in antioxidants. I will admit, however, that buying them regularly can get expensive. Buying frozen berries in bulk is a bit cheaper.
- **Citrus Fruits (Lemons, Oranges):** Frequently used in my dressings and as flavor enhancers, these fruits are rich in vitamin C and flavonoids. Some people have digestive sensitivites to citrus, so it's best to get tested!

Proteins

- **Tofu:** Used in a handful of breakfast and lunch/dinner recipes, tofu provides plant-based protein alternative and is very versatile. There are some anti-inflammatory books that shy away from soy altogether. This really comes down to *bioindividuality* - how a particular food interacts with your specific biochemistry. For me, soy is fine. For you, it may not be. Get tested. Please.
- **Wild-Caught Salmon:** Salmon appears in multiple recipes for its omega-3 content. Unfortunately, salmon does not come cheap. I am sorry about this. Proteins are tricky when it comes to anti-inflammatory diets. I generally suggest you eat plant-based proteins as much as possible.
- **Chicken/Turkey:** You'll find both throughout this book. On the "scale" of animal-based proteins to eat or avoid, chicken and turkey fall in the middle. From an anti-inflammation perspective, red meats are generally more inflammatory than white meats and are on the "eat sparingly" side of the scale, while plant-based proteins are on the "eat regularly" side of the scale. For me, I enjoy a steak every now and again and follow the age-old rule: I eat animal proteins in moderation and on occasion. Respect to those who have adopted a vegetarian or vegan diet. I'm not there, yet.

Sweeteners

- **Maple & Agave Syrup (foundational):** Used in breakfast and snack recipes as natural sweeteners with lower glycemic impact

Beverages

- **Coconut Milk:** Frequently used in soups and curries, offering a rich texture and healthy fats.
- **Coffee (foundational):** Found in a few recipes. Drinking black coffee is the most beneficial. Coffee contains polyphenols, which are compounds that may prevent free radicals from causing damage that can lead to inflammation. Some polyphenols may also block the production of inflammatory compounds by inhibiting enzymes and gene expression.
- **Green Tea (foundational):** Not found in any of my recipes, but I heartily recommend drinking green tea as much as possible. Green tea contains polyphenols, which are plant-based compounds that have anti-inflammatory properties. Epigallocatechin-3-gallate (EGCG) is the most potent polyphenol in green tea, which is also found in fruts and nuts.

BENEFICIAL FOOD & NUTRIENT PAIRINGS

KADE Vitamins + Healthy Fats

KADE stands for vitamins K, A, D, and E. KADE vitamins are fat soluble, meaning that they dissolve (and are better absorbed) in fats and oils. So, when it comes to enjoying salads and vegetables like carrots, sweet potatoes, lettuce, and tomatoes, you can enhance their nutritional value by simply pairing them with a flavorful oil-based dressings, crunchy nuts or seeds, creamy avocado, or delicious spreads like hummus or guacamole. These additions will not only enhance the taste but also help your body absorb the vitamins they offer. You'll see these pairings throughout the book.

Iron + Vitamin C

The vitamin C in bell peppers works wonders when it comes to boosting the absorption of iron in spinach, giving you that extra energy you need. Not a fan of peppers? Strawberries, broccoli, and citrus fruits are excellent alternatives for achieving the same desired outcome, as they are all abundant in vitamin C. How about trying a delicious strawberry spinach salad (I have a recipe for that later)!

Calcium + Vitamin D

Dark leafy greens and salmon are a great combination. Incorporating dark leafy greens like kale, arugula, Swiss chard, basil, and parsley into your diet can provide you with bone-strengthening minerals. Most of these foods are found in the recipes to come. For optimal absorption and utilization, it's important to pair these greens, which are rich in calcium, with vitamin D. Pairing foods that are high in vitamin D (such as wild salmon, pasture-raised egg yolks, and crimini mushrooms) with calcium-rich greens can help you maximize the benefits of both nutrients.

Green Tea + Lemon

Green tea and lemon make a delightful combination. Green tea is known for its abundance of catechins, which are powerful antioxidants that offer anti-aging benefits, boost brain function, and promote a healthy heart. Adding a squeeze of lemon, rich in vitamin C, will greatly enhance the bioavailability of these compounds.

Green Tea + Pepper

Pairing a cup of green tea with a meal that includes black pepper can boost the body's ability to absorb catechin, which is plentiful in green tea. These polyphenols known as catechins have powerful anti-inflammatory and antimicrobial properties, which are thought to enhance the immune system.

Tomatoes + Olive Oil

Every tomato contains lycopene, a powerful antioxidant that helps fight against diseases. One potential benefit of lycopene is its ability to potentially reduce the risk of prostate cancer. When it comes to tomatoes, cooking them and adding a drizzle of olive oil can boost the body's ability to absorb the lycopene. Take caution, however, becuase tomatoes are in the nightshade family of fruits, which many have trouble digesting.

Vinegar + Olive Oil

Incorporating extra virgin olive oil, red wine, or apple cider vinegar into a dressing for a leafy green salad can enhance the antioxidant content.

Eggs + Vegetables

Some antioxidants called carotenoids can be found in eggs, as well as in orange and red vegetables and dark, leafy greens. However, when these vegetables are combined, the carotenoid content increases significantly, ranging from three to nine times higher.

Dark Chocolate + Raspberries

For dark chocolate enthusiasts, here's some exciting news: the polyphenols found in dark chocolate have been found to exhibit enhanced activity when paired with raspberries. Rejoice! (in moderation). Remember to stick with +70% dark chocolate, and significantly limit your intake of refined sugars.

ANTI-INFLAMMATORY SUPERFOODS

There are a handful of "superfoods" with anti-inflammatory properties. Let's look at the most common:

Berries

Berries are a great source of fiber, vitamins, and minerals. They contain high levels of antioxidants that reduce inflammation, such as quercetin, anthocyanins, and Vitamin C. Take a look at the chart on the next page:

Per ½ Cup	Blackberries	Blueberries	Raspberries	Strawberries
Primary Antioxidants	Anthocyanins.	Ellagic acid, anthocyanidins.	Anthocyanidins, quercetin,	Ellagic acid, Ellagitannins, Procyanidins.
Minerals (mg)	Calcium (24), potassium (154), sodium (1), phosphorous (24), magnesium (18).	Calcium (29), potassium (122), phosphorous (29), magnesium (11).	Calcium (16), potassium (185), phosphorous (45), magnesium (21).	Calcium (20), potassium (197), sodium (1), phosphorous (29), magnesium (14).
Omega Fatty Acids (mg)	Omega-3 (0.1), Omega-6 (0.2).	Omega-3 (0.2), Omega-6 (0.2).	Omega-3 (0.1), Omega-6 (0.2).	Omega-3 (0.1), Omega-6 (0.1).
Vitamins (mg)	A (38), B (96), C (7), E (2.4).	A (96), B (12), C (12), E (2).	A (3), B, (35), C (17), E (2)	A (10), B (70) C (69), E (7).

Cherries

Cherries have anti-inflammatory and antioxidant components that can help to reduce inflammation by altering how your blood interprets anti-inflammatory indicators. Whole dark cherries, dark cherry juice, and dried cherries are delicious, and what you should target.

Cherries (per ½ cup)	
Primary Antioxidants	Polyphenols
Minerals (mg)	Calcium (18), potassium (220), phosphorous (25), magnesium (13).
Vitamins (mg)	A (32), B (27), C (4), E (6).

Dark Chocolate

When including dark chocolate in your anti-inflammatory diet, quality, and cocoa percentage are crucial considerations. Aside from being a delectable treat with fewer calories than milk chocolate, dark chocolate provides several health benefits. Dark chocolate with a cocoa percentage of 70% or above contains antioxidants, flavonoids, and free radicals with anti-inflammatory qualities. They aid in the healing of damaged cells in the body. Dark chocolate also naturally has healthy fat but is often combined with non-beneficial sugars and fats. Keep in mind - moderation is required to reap the anti-inflammatory benefits here.

Dark Chocolate (per ½ cup)	
Primary Antioxidants	Phenolic, catechin, epicatechin, procyanidins.
Minerals (mg)	Calcium (13), potassium (350), sodium (4), phosphorous (66), magnesium (62).
Omega Fatty Acids (mg)	Omega-3 (1), Omega-6 (15).
Vitamins (mg)	A (61), B (41), E (0.3).

Extra Virgin Olive Oil

Olive oil has a significant amount of monounsaturated fatty acids. Monounsaturated fats, when used as a replacement for saturated fat, aid in reducing levels of "bad" LDL cholesterol. Extra virgin olive oil also possesses anti-inflammatory properties, which contribute significantly to its health-promoting effects. The anti-inflammatory properties of olive oil are attributed to its primary antioxidant, oleocanthal. This antioxidant exhibits similar anti-inflammatory properties to ibuprofen, a nonsteroidal anti-inflammatory medication. Furthermore, the presence of antioxidants in olive oil has the potential to diminish oxidative harm caused by free radicals, which are widely thought to contribute to the development of cancer. Studies have also demonstrated that oleic acid, the primary fatty acid found in olive oil, has the ability to decrease the presence of inflammatory indicators such C-reactive protein (CRP).

Per 1/2 cup:	Extra Virgin Olive Oil
Primary Antioxidants	Oleocanthal, secoiridoids, lignans, and flavones
Omega Fatty Acids (mg)	Omega-3 (1), Omega-6 (7).
Vitamins (mg)	E (17).

Fatty Fish

Fatty fish, such as mackerel, salmon, sardines, and tuna, contain omega-3 fatty acids, which reduce inflammation by lowering blood pressure, reducing plaque build-up, and act as a natural blood thinner.

Per 1/2 cup:	Mackerel	Salmon	Sardine	Tuna

Primary Antioxidants	Catalase, glutathione peroxidase, peptides, superoxide dismutase, ubiquinones.	Catalase, glutathione peroxidase, peptides, superoxide dismutase, ubiquinones.	Catalase, glutathione peroxidase, peptides, superoxide dismutase, ubiquinones.	Catalase, glutathione peroxidase, peptides, superoxide dismutase, ubiquinones.
Minerals (mg)	Calcium (19), potassium (450), sodium (74), phosphorous (260), magnesium (29).	Calcium (7), potassium (451), sodium (46), phosphorous (227), magnesium (26).	Calcium (7), potassium (451), sodium (46), phosphorous (227), magnesium (26).	Calcium (7), potassium (451), sodium (46), phosphorous (227), magnesium (26).
Omega Fatty Acids (mg)	Omega-3 (1), Omega-6 (1), eicosapentaenoic acid (EPA) (0.5), docosahexaenoic acid (DHA) (1)	Omega-3 (2.6), Omega-6 (2.5), EPA (1) DHA (1)	Omega-3 (2.6), Omega-6 (2.5), EPA (450) DHA (740)	Omega-3 (3), Omega-6 (1), EPA (1) DHA (710)
Vitamins (mg)	A (2), B (10), D (7), E (0.6).	A (52), B (14), D (7), E (1).	A (52), B (14), D (7), E (1).	A (372), B (15), D (2), E (1).

Garlic and Onions

Garlic is often used as a condiment, and it also contains organosulfur, a compound rich in antioxidants. Organosulfur reduces inflammation by controlling other minerals in your blood that produce it when activated by your environment (pollen, dust, abrasive chemicals, etc.). Onion contains Quercetin, which, like garlic, modulates your body's inflammation and sensitivity to stimuli.

Per 1/2 cup	Garlic	Onions
Primary Antioxidants	Allicin	Quercetin
Minerals (mg)	Calcium (19), potassium (620), sodium (4), phosphorous (170), magnesium (25).	Calcium (11), potassium (475), sodium (40), phosphorous (266), magnesium (39).
Omega Fatty Acids (mg)	Omega-3 (1), Omega-6 (1).	Omega-3 (0.3), Omega-6 (0.1).
Vitamins (mg)	B (2), C (17)	A (372), B (6), D (2), E (1)

Dark Leafy Greens

Leafy greens are nutrient dense, and have a compound called quercetin. "Quercetin has the ability to act like anti-inflammatory drugs (aspirin, ibuprofen) and block the effects of tumor necrosis factor (TNF), which is usually found in high levels in people with rheumatoid arthritis" (Kowalczyk).

Per 1/2 cup:	Collard greens	Kale	Spinach
Primary Antioxidants	Lutein, zeaxanthin.	Lutein, zeaxanthin.	Lutein, coumaric acid, ferulic acid.
Minerals (in milligram)	Calcium (33), potassium (260), sodium (8), phosphorous (25), magnesium (11).	Calcium (157), potassium (530), sodium (12), phosphorous (56), magnesium 30).	Calcium (19), potassium (450), sodium (74), phosphorous (260), magnesium (29).
Omega Fatty Acids (mg)	Omega-3 (0.1) Omega-6 (1).	Omega-3 (0.1) Omega-6 (1).	Omega-3 (0.1)

Nuts and Seeds

The nuts and seeds listed below are strong in omega-3 and fiber.

Per 1/2 cup:	Almonds	Walnuts	Chia Seeds	Flax Seeds
Main Antioxidants	Polyphenol	Polyphenol	Chlorogenic acid, caffeic acid, myricetin, quercetin, kaempferol.	Coumaric acid, ferulic acid, cyanogenic glycosides, phytosterols, lignans.
Minerals (mg)	Calcium (19), potassium (450), sodium (74), phosphorous (260), magnesium (29).	Calcium (84), potassium (380), phosphorous (310), magnesium (130).	Calcium (545), potassium (640), phosphorous (645), magnesium (320).	Calcium (19), potassium (450), sodium (74), phosphorous (260), magnesium (29).
Omega Fatty Acids (mg)	Omega-6 (11).	Omega-3 (6), Omega-6 (31).	Omega-3 (19), Omega-6 (6).	Omega-3 (26), Omega-6 (6).
Vitamins (mg)	B (4), C (1), E (23)	B (2), C (1), E (1)	B (2), C (2),	B (6), C (1), E (1)

Turmeric

Turmeric, a member of the ginger family, contains a high concentration of antioxidants and anti-inflammatory compounds. Unlike the other items on this list, turmeric may be ground into a paste and applied directly to the skin for topical anti-inflammatory treatment. Turmeric has been demonstrated to effectively reduce inflammation and swelling, joint pain, and enlarged kidneys. Turmeric contains curcumin, a chemical that has potent anti-inflammatory actions. It can also be added to tea to boost its anti-inflammatory properties.

Per 1/2 cup:	Turmeric
Primary Antioxidants	Curcumin
Minerals (mg)	Calcium (19), potassium (450), phosphorous (260), magnesium (29)
Omega Fatty Acids (mg)	Omega-6 (1)
Vitamins (mg)	B (2), C (1), E (4)

Whole Grains

Whole grains provide a variety of health benefits because they're less processed than refined grains (white rice, plain pasta, etc.), and have retained more of their mineral, fiber, and vitamin content. Do note, however, as healthy as they are, whole grains are carbohydrates at the end of the day and should be eaten in moderation.

Per 1/2 cup:	Brown rice	Millet	Oats	Quinoa
Primary Antioxidants	Phenolics, flavonoids.	Tannin, phytic acid, flavonoids.	Phytic acid, phenolic compounds, avenanthramides	Quercetin, kaempferol.
Minerals (mg)	Calcium (11), potassium (193), sodium (3), phosphorous (282), magnesium (115).	Calcium (19), potassium (450), sodium (74), phosphorous (260), magnesium (29).	Calcium (101), potassium (210), sodium (121), phosphorous (170), magnesium (35).	Calcium (19), potassium (450), sodium (74), phosphorous (260), magnesium (29).
Omega Fatty Acids (mg)	Omega-6 (1).	Omega-3 (0.1), Omega-6 (1.4).	Omega-6 (0.5).	Omega-3 (0.3), Omega-6 (2.4).

Vitamins (mg)	B (6).	B (4) E (0.1)	A (19), B (1), D (0.1), E (0.1)	B (2), E (2.3)

ANTI-INFLAMMATORY SPICES & HERBS

Certain spices and herbs can supercharge your anti-inflammatory journey. You'll find that most (if not all) recipes in this book contain at least one beneficial spice or herb, and many recipes combine spices and herbs for powerful anti-inflammatory multiplier effects!

Basil

Basil is packed with healthy compounds including ascorbic acid, aldehydes, alkaloids, fatty acids like omega-3 and 6, glycosides, phenols, saponins, tannins, and terpenes. Basil also includes essential oils and phytonutrients with anti-inflammatory properties, and eugenol, which has been studied for its ability to block the action of an enzyme in the body that promotes inflammation. In addition to their anti-inflammatory properties, each of these components contributes to reducing the effects of health conditions like arthritis, hypertension, and type 2 diabetes. Basil also boosts the immune system.

Cinnamon

Cinnamon, a popular spice with a long history of medicinal use, also exhibits potent anti-inflammatory properties primarily attributed to its bioactive compounds, including cinnamaldehyde and procyanidins. These compounds exert anti-inflammatory effects by inhibiting the activity of pro-inflammatory enzymes like cyclooxygenase (COX) and lipoxygenase (LOX), thereby reducing the production of inflammatory mediators such as prostaglandins and leukotrienes. Moreover, cinnamon compounds modulate inflammatory signaling pathways such as nuclear factor-kappa B (NF-B) and mitogen-activated protein kinases (MAPKs), leading to decreased expression of inflammatory cytokines. Additionally, cinnamon's antioxidant activity helps neutralize free radicals and reduce oxidative stress, which contributes to its anti-inflammatory effects.

Garlic

Garlic, renowned for its culinary and medicinal properties, also boasts impressive anti-inflammatory effects owing to its sulfur-containing compounds like allicin, diallyl sulfide, and diallyl disulfide. These compounds exhibit anti-inflammatory actions by inhibiting the activity of pro-inflammatory enzymes such as cyclooxygenase (COX) and lipoxygenase (LOX), thus reducing the production of inflammatory mediators like prostaglandins and leukotrienes. Furthermore, garlic compounds interfere with the activation of nuclear factor-kappa B (NF-B), a key regulator of inflammation, and downregulate the expression of inflammatory cytokines. Additionally, garlic's antioxidant properties help combat oxidative stress, which is closely linked to inflammation.

Ginger

Ginger possesses notable anti-inflammatory properties primarily attributed to its bioactive compounds, such as gingerol, shogaol, and paradol. These compounds inhibit the production of pro-inflammatory molecules like prostaglandins and leukotrienes by suppressing enzymes like cyclooxygenase (COX) and lipoxygenase (LOX). Additionally, gingerols have been found to modulate inflammatory signaling pathways, including nuclear factor-kappa B (NF-B) and mitogen-activated protein kinases (MAPKs), thereby reducing the expression of inflammatory cytokines. Moreover, ginger exhibits antioxidant effects, scavenging free radicals and reducing oxidative stress, which contributes to its anti-inflammatory properties.

Turmeric

You're going to hear a lot about turmeric in this book. There are many recipes that utilize it. Turmeric owes its anti-inflammatory properties primarily to its active compound, curcumin. Curcumin possesses potent anti-inflammatory effects by inhibiting various molecules and enzymes involved in the inflammatory process, such as cyclooxygenase-2 (COX-2), lipoxygenase (LOX), nuclear factor-kappa B (NF-B), and cytokines like tumor necrosis factor-alpha (TNF-) and interleukins. It also scavenges free radicals and reduces oxidative stress, which contributes to inflammation. Moreover, curcumin modulates signaling pathways involved in inflammation, exerting a multifaceted approach to mitigating inflammatory responses in the body.

Black Pepper

Black pepper, often used as a spice and traditional medicine, contains a bioactive compound called piperine, which contributes to its anti-inflammatory properties. Piperine inhibits the activity of inflammatory enzymes like cyclooxygenase (COX) and lipoxygenase (LOX), thereby reducing the production of inflammatory mediators such as prostaglandins and leukotrienes. Additionally, piperine has been found to suppress the activation of nuclear factor-kappa B (NF-B), a key regulator of inflammation, and decrease the expression of inflammatory cytokines. Furthermore, black pepper exhibits antioxidant activity, scavenging free radicals and reducing oxidative stress, which is closely linked to inflammation.

Cayenne Pepper

Cayenne pepper contains capsaicin, a compound that has been shown to inhibit the production of substance P, a neuropeptide involved in inflammation. Capsaicin also exerts anti-inflammatory effects by modulating NF-B activation and reducing the expression of inflammatory cytokines, contributing to its potential therapeutic value in inflammatory conditions.

Cloves

Cloves are rich in eugenol, a compound with notable anti-inflammatory properties. Eugenol inhibits inflammatory enzymes like COX and LOX, thus reducing the production of prostaglandins and leukotrienes. Moreover, cloves possess antioxidant activity, which helps alleviate oxidative stress and inflammation-related damage in the body.

Rosemary

Rosemary contains rosmarinic acid and carnosic acid, compounds known for their anti-inflammatory effects. Rosmarinic acid inhibits inflammatory enzymes and modulates inflammatory signaling pathways, leading to reduced production of inflammatory mediators. Additionally, rosemary's antioxidant properties contribute to its ability to combat inflammation and oxidative stress.

Oregano

Oregano is rich in carvacrol and thymol, two compounds with potent anti-inflammatory properties. Carvacrol and thymol inhibit inflammatory enzymes like COX and LOX, thereby reducing the synthesis of prostaglandins and leukotrienes. Oregano also exhibits antioxidant activity, which helps mitigate inflammation-induced oxidative damage.

PRO-INFLAMMATORY FOODS TO AVOID

Here are some foods to consider minimizing or avoiding altogether. As I started this chapter by saying: you will need to be intentional about your life choices if you're serious about reducing your inflammation. Diet is a huge factor and it's not just about adding beneficial nutrients. You also will need to remove foods and substances that cause harm.

Processed Foods

Processed foods, such as fast food, packaged snacks, and sugary treats, often contain high levels of unhealthy fats, sugars, and refined carbohydrates, all of which can promote inflammation when consumed in excess.

Refined Carbohydrates

Foods made with refined grains, such as white bread, white rice, and pastries, can spike blood sugar levels and promote inflammation. Opt for whole grains like brown rice, quinoa, oats, and whole wheat bread instead.

Added Sugars

Foods and beverages with added sugars, such as sodas, sweets, candies, and sugary snacks, can trigger inflammation and contribute to various health problems. Try to reduce your intake of sugary foods and opt for naturally sweet alternatives like fruits.

Trans Fats

Trans fats, often found in fried foods, baked goods, margarine, and processed snacks, are known to promote inflammation and increase the risk of heart disease. Check food labels and avoid products that contain partially hydrogenated oils.

Saturated Fats

While some sources of saturated fats, such as coconut oil and dairy, may have neutral or even beneficial effects, excessive intake of saturated fats from sources like fatty meats and full-fat dairy products can contribute to inflammation. Choose lean protein sources and limit high-fat dairy products.

Processed Meats

Processed meats like hot dogs, sausages, bacon, and deli meats often contain additives and preservatives that can trigger inflammation. Limit your intake of processed meats and opt for leaner protein sources like poultry, fish, and legumes.

Alcohol

Excessive alcohol consumption can disrupt gut health, increase inflammation, and weaken the immune system. Limit your intake of alcohol and opt for healthier alternatives like water, herbal teas, or sparkling water flavored with fruit.

Artificial Additives

Food additives like artificial sweeteners, preservatives, and colorings may trigger inflammatory responses in some individuals. Try to minimize your intake of processed foods and choose whole, minimally processed options whenever possible.

Highly Processed Oils

Certain oils high in omega-6 fatty acids, such as corn oil, soybean oil, and sunflower oil, can promote inflammation when consumed in excess. Instead, choose healthier fats like olive oil, avocado oil, and flaxseed oil.

Excessive Salt

High sodium intake from processed and packaged foods can contribute to inflammation and increase the risk of conditions like high blood pressure and heart disease. Limit your consumption of salty snacks, canned soups, and processed foods, and opt for fresh, whole foods seasoned with herbs and spices instead.

DAIRY FOODS

I'll spend some time explaining the dairy foods you'll likely need to limit. This one is tough for me because I LOVE dairy products but really did need to limit my intake. Individual tolerance to dairy foods is influenced by various factors, including genetics, lactase enzyme activity (which breaks down lactose, the sugar found in dairy), gut microbiota composition, and personal health history. Ultimately, whether someone can digest dairy foods comfortably depends on their unique physiological factors and tolerances. It's essential for individuals to listen to their bodies and pay attention to how they feel after consuming dairy products and make dietary choices that best support their health and well-being.

Avoid Full-Fat or No-Fat Dairy Products

Full-fat dairy products like whole milk, cream, cheese, and butter are high in saturated fats, which have been associated with increased inflammation and risk of chronic diseases like heart disease. Fat-free dairy products are known to cause digestive issues as well. I hate to say this, but you severly limit or eliminate cow milk from your diet altogether.

Avoid Sweetened Dairy Products

Flavored yogurts, sweetened milk beverages, and dessert-style dairy products like ice cream and pudding often contain added sugars, which can promote inflammation and contribute to health problems. Choose unsweetened versions of cashew, almond, or coconut yogurts instead.

Avoid Processed Dairy Foods

Processed dairy foods like processed cheese slices, cheese spreads, and flavored cream cheeses may contain additives, preservatives, and other ingredients that can trigger inflammation in some individuals. Opt for natural, minimally processed forms of vegan substitutes whenever possible.

Avoid Creamy Sauces and Dressings

Cream-based sauces, dressings, and dips made with dairy products like sour cream and mayonnaise can be high in unhealthy fats and calories, as well as additives and preservatives. Choose lighter, non-dairy options or make your own dressings and sauces using healthier ingredients.

Avoid High-Lactose Foods

Some individuals may be lactose intolerant or have difficulty digesting lactose, the sugar found in milk and dairy products (like me). High-lactose dairy foods like milk, soft cheeses, and ice cream (eeek!) can cause digestive discomfort and inflammation in these individuals. Consider lactose-free or vegan options if you experience symptoms like bloating, gas, or diarrhea after consuming dairy.

Avoid Processed Dairy Alternatives

While dairy alternatives like plant-based milks (soy, almond, coconut) and dairy-free cheeses can be suitable alternatives for individuals with lactose intolerance or dairy allergies, some processed dairy alternatives may contain additives, sweeteners, and other ingredients that can trigger inflammation. Choose unsweetened, minimally processed options when selecting dairy alternatives.

Avoid Excessive Dairy Consumption

Consuming excessive amounts of dairy products, regardless of type, can contribute to inflammation and health issues in some individuals. Practice moderation and balance in your dairy intake and consider consulting with a healthcare professional or registered dietitian if you have concerns or specific dietary needs.

BE CAREFUL OF PESTICIDES

Food production is often rife with pesticides to maintain quality, but these pesticides aren't always removed from the food before being sold to the retailer. The Environmental Working Group (ewg.org) is responsible for documenting and advising companies about fresh produce and the amount of pesticides on certain foods. They have two important lists for your to remember: the **Dirty Dozen** and the **Clean Fifteen**.

The Dirty Dozen is a list of produce with the highest amount of pesticide residue, while the Clean Fifteen is a list of the fruits and vegetables with the lowest amount of residue. The best way to mitigate the Dirty Dozen is to buy organic products where possible and wash your produce with apple cider vinegar and water before consumption. Baking soda and water is also known to remove surface level contaminants.

The Dirty Dozen(ish) (wash well!) apples, blueberries, cherries, collard greens, kale, mustard greens, grapes, green beans, nectarines, peaches, pears, peppers (bell and hot), spinach, strawberries

The Clean Fifteen (still wash well), asparagus, avocados, cabbage, carrots, honeydew melon, kiwi, mangos, mushrooms, onions, papaya, pineapple, sweet corn, sweet peas, sweet potatoes, watermelon

DECIPHERING RECIPE SYMBOLS

The recipes in this book include a series of symbols that indicate whether or not they are dairy-free, gluten-free, low sugar, vegetarian, vegan, or low carb. Here's what they look like:

Dairy free. I define "dairy free" as not containing any dairy ingredients, including milk, milk products, or milk by-products from mammals like cows, sheep, and goats.

Gluten free. I define "gluten free" the same as the FDA. The recipe does not contain wheat, rye, barley, or crossbreeds of these grains.

Low carb Low carb, in this case, means the recipe has less than 10g of total carbohydrates.

Low sugar. Low sugar, in this case, means the recipe has less than 10g of total sugar.

Paleo. The paleo symbol means that a recipe is made with ingredients that align with the paleo diet, which generally excludes processed foods and ingredients like grains, dairy, and refined sugar. The paleo diet focuses on foods that people could obtain through hunting and gathering, such as fruits, vegetables, lean meats, fish, eggs, nuts, and seeds

Vegan. A recipe is vegan if it doesn't intentionally use any animal products or by-products in the ingredients or manufacturing process. This includes meat, fish, fowl, eggs, dairy, honey, insects, and sugar filtered with bone char.

Vegetarian. A recipe is vegetarian if it doesn't contain meat, poultry, seafood, or by-products of animal slaughter.

CHAPTER 3:
BREAKFAST RECIPES

NO-BAKE GRANOLA BITES

Time: ~8-10 hours
Serving size: 20 bites

Nothing easier than this recipe. I say that it makes 20 servings (20 bites), but your bite sizes may vary. I tend to make them on the larger side. You can also easily vary the sugar content of this recipe by adding less cranberries and using ¼ cup of sweetener.

Nutritional Information (Approximate per 1 serving):
Calories: 200 | Protein: 4g | Fat: 12g | Carbs: 21g | Fiber: 4g

Beneficial Nutrients & Anti-Inflammatories:

Quick oats: Beta-glucan | Dried cranberries: Antioxidants (quercetin) | Coconut flakes: Medium-chain triglycerides (MCTs) | Chopped nuts: Omega-3 fatty acids, Vitamin E | Nut butter (almond butter): Omega-3 fatty acids, Vitamin E | Ground flaxseed: Omega-3 fatty acids (ALA), Lignans | Coconut oil: Medium-chain triglycerides (MCTs) | Vanilla extract: Antioxidants

Ingredients:

- 1 ½ cups (156g) quick oats (Bob's Red Mill is a recommended brand. They don't use chemicals to process their oats)
- 1 cup (~325g) combination of dried cranberries, coconut flakes, and chopped nuts (your choice)
- 1 cup (240g) creamy nut butter (I like almond butter)
- 1 cup (175g) ground flaxseed
- 1/2 cup (60g) pumpkin seeds
- 1/2 cup (175g) agave syrup
- 2/3 cup (27g) crispy rice cereal
- 2 tbsp (27g) coconut oil. If you have a sensitivity to coconut oil, try avocado oil.
- 2 tsp (8.5g) vanilla extract

Directions:

1. Place all the ingredients in a mixing bowl and mix well, making sure to be gentle so that you don't crush the crispy rice.
2. Use a spoon or your hands and shape the mixture into small balls.
3. Place on a wax paper lined tray and in the fridge for 8-10 hours. If you're hungry sooner rather than later, the minimum time I recommend for eating is 2 hours, but they get nice and solid after about 8 hours.

APPLE BREAKFAST HASH

Time: 30 minutes
Serving size: 4

You can't beat a delicious breakfast hash. You can easily substitute the ground turkey with chopped tofu. This one is packed with protein and various herbs and spices that are loaded up with anti-inflammatory compounds. Enjoy!

Nutritional Information (Approximate per 1 serving):
Calories: 300 kcal | Protein: 20g | Carbohydrates: 20g | Dietary Fiber: 5g | Sugars: 8g | Fat: 15g | Saturated Fat: 3g | Sodium: 350mg

Beneficial Nutrients & Anti-Inflammatories:

Olive Oil/Avocado Oil: Monounsaturated fats, antioxidants | Sweet Potato: Beta-carotene, vitamins A and C | Apple: Quercetin, vitamin C | Turmeric: Curcumin | Cumin: Cuminaldehyde, other antioxidants | Cinnamon: Cinnamaldehyde, other antioxidants | Black Pepper: Piperine | Spinach/Kale: Vitamins A, C, K, antioxidants | Avocado: Monounsaturated fats, vitamin E, antioxidants

....

Ingredients:

- 1 tablespoon (13.3g) olive oil or avocado oil
- (optional) 1 pound (16oz) ground turkey, ground chicken, or chopped tofu
- 1 medium sweet potato (142g), peeled and diced
- 1 apple (~160g), cored and diced (Granny Smith are my choice)
- 1 small onion (~100g), diced
- 1 medium bell pepper (170g), diced (I use yellow or red)
- 1 teaspoon (3g) ground turmeric
- 1/2 teaspoon (1.5g) ground cumin
- 1/2 teaspoon (1g) ground cinnamon
- 1/2 teaspoon (1.5g) ground black pepper (enhances turmeric absorption)
- 1/2 teaspoon (3g) salt (to taste)
- 1/4 teaspoon (.75g) red pepper flakes (optional, for a bit of heat)
- 1 cup baby spinach (30g) or kale (67g), chopped
- Fresh parsley or cilantro, chopped (for garnish)
- 1 avocado, sliced (for serving)

....

Directions:

1. Heat the olive oil or avocado oil in a large skillet over medium heat.
2. Add the ground turkey and cook, breaking it apart with a spoon, until it is browned and cooked through, about 5-7 minutes.
3. Add the diced sweet potato, apple, onion, and bell pepper to the skillet. Cook, stirring occasionally, until the vegetables are tender, about 10-12 minutes.
4. Stir in the ground turmeric, cumin, cinnamon, black pepper, salt, and red pepper flakes (if using). Cook for another 2-3 minutes, until the spices are well combined and fragrant.
5. Add the chopped spinach or kale to the skillet and cook until wilted, about 2-3 minutes.
6. Remove from heat and garnish with fresh parsley or cilantro.
7. Serve the hash with sliced avocado on top.

BOB'S OATMEAL WITH WALNUTS & GOJI BERRIES

Time: 15 minutes
Serving size: 2

I like just about every oatmeal recipe. This one is hearty and delicious, and the goji berries add a unique tang. Remember the key to eating any oatmeal recipe is to watch your portion sizing. Oats are a great complex carbohydrate, but a carbohydrate none-the-less.

Nutritional Information (Approximate per 1 serving):

Calories: 400 kcal | Protein: 12g | Carbohydrates: 58g | Dietary Fiber: 9g | Sugars: 15g (including added sweetener and dried goji berries) | Fat: 17g | Saturated Fat: 2g | Sodium: 175mg

Beneficial Nutrients & Anti-Inflammatories:

Walnuts: Omega-3 fatty acids (alpha-linolenic acid), polyphenols | Goji Berries: Zeaxanthin, vitamin C | Chia Seeds: Omega-3 fatty acids (alpha-linolenic acid), fiber | Cinnamon: Cinnamaldehyde, other antioxidants

ANTI-INFLAMMATORY DIET & COOKBOOK

Ingredients:

- 1 cup (156g) rolled oats (Bob's Red Mill is a recommended brand. They don't use chemicals to process their oats)
- 2 cups (472g) water or unsweetened almond milk (488g; or a combination of both)
- 1/4 teaspoon (1.5g) salt
- 1/2 teaspoon (1g) ground cinnamon
- 1/4 cup (29g) chopped walnuts
- 1/4 cup (29g) dried goji berries (note: goji berries are part of the nightshade family of fruits. You can substitute with dried cranberries for those with associated sensitivities.
- 1 tablespoon (10g) chia seeds (optional, for added nutrients)
- 2 tablespoons (40g) maple syrup (to taste)
- 1 teaspoon (4.2g) vanilla extract (optional)
- Fresh fruit for topping (optional, such as banana slices, berries, or apple slices)

Directions:

1. In a medium saucepan, bring the water or almond milk to a boil.
2. Stir in the rolled oats and salt. Reduce the heat to medium-low and simmer, stirring occasionally, until the oats are tender and the mixture has thickened, about 5-7 minutes.
3. Add the ground cinnamon and vanilla extract (if using), and stir to combine.
4. Remove the oatmeal from the heat and stir in the chopped walnuts, goji berries, and chia seeds (if using).
5. Taste and add honey or maple syrup to sweeten, adjusting to your preference
6. Divide the oatmeal into bowls and top with fresh fruit if desired.
7. Serve immediately and enjoy!

CHERRY-MOCHA SMOOTHIE

Time: 10 minutes
Serving size: 2

If you like chocolate, coffee, and cherries, and the thought of all of them together in the same drink appeals to you, this is your drink. If you want to significantly reduce total sugar, you don't need the banana or chocolate shavings. I've included their nutritional information in the recipe. Cutting them out brings the total sugar per serving to less than 10g.

Nutritional Information (Approximate per 1 serving):

Calories: 350 | Carbs: 34g | Fiber: 7g | Sugars: 21g (using all ingredients) | Protein: 13g | Fat: 12g | Saturated Fat: 2g | Cholesterol: 2mg | Sodium: 154mg

Beneficial Nutrients & Anti-Inflammatories:

Dark Sweet Cherries: antioxidants, anthocyanins; Almonds: healthy fats, vitamin E; Dark Chocolate: flavonoids; Cocoa Powder: polyphenols; Banana: vitamin C, vitamin B6, and fiber.

Ingredients:

- 1 cup (155g) frozen unsweetened (pitted) dark cherries
- 1 cup (244g) unsweetened chocolate almond milk (or regular unsweetened almond milk if you cannot fine unsweetened chocolate)
- 1 tbsp (6g) +70% dark chocolate shavings (optional)
- 1 tsp (2g) instant espresso coffee powder
- 1 tsp (4.2g) vanilla
- 2 cups (200g) ice cubes
- 2 tbsp (30g) almond butter
- 2 tbsp (15g) unsweetened cocoa powder
- 3/4 cup (184g) vanilla cashew yogurt (low sugar variety)
- 1/2 banana (~60g; optional)
- Water

Directions:

1. Place all ingredients, except the chocolate shavings, into a blender and blend until smooth. Add water to adjust the consistency to your liking.
2. Pour into tall glasses, top with the shavings. Enjoy!

CHIA SEED BREAKFAST PUDDING WITH BERRIES

Time: 12 hours
Serving size: 4

I mean, who doesn't love pudding? I love pudding. You love pudding. This simple recipe is cool, refreshing, and has a touch of warmth from the cinnamon and great texture from the chia seeds. I combine everything after dinner, stir once before bed, and let set overnight.

Nutritional Information (Approximate per 1 serving):

Calories: 230 | Carbohydrates: 18g | Protein: 7g | Fat: 9g | Sodium: 91mg |

Potassium: 96mg | Fiber: 13g | Sugar: 11g

Beneficial Nutrients & Anti-Inflammatories:

Coconut/Almond Milk: healthy fats, antioxidants, vitamin E; Chia Seeds: omega-3 fatty acids, fiber, and antioxidants; Maple Syrup: antioxidants; Cinnamon: antioxidants; Berries: antioxidants and vitamins.

....

Ingredients:

- 2 cups coconut milk (456g) or almond milk (488g)
- 1/2 cup (118g) water
- 1/2 cup (81g) chia seeds
- 1/4 cup (83g) maple syrup
- 1 tsp (4.2g) vanilla
- 1 tbsp (7.8g) cinnamon
- 1/8 teaspoon (.74g) salt
- Berries (your choice) and coconut flakes

....

Directions:

1. Combine everything except the berries and coconut flakes in a medium-sized bowl. Mix well.
2. Cover the bowl and set it in the refrigerator for 2 hours. After 2 hours, stir well and place back into the refrigerator. Let it set overnight.
3. Serve pudding with fresh berries and a sprinkling of coconut on top.

EGG SALAD, AVOCADO & EZEKIEL TOAST

Time: 20-60 minutes
Serving size: 8

Simple, healthy, delicious. This one is a go-to in our home. The egg salad recipe uses paleo ingredients, and the Ezekiel Bread is a sprouted grain variety and a terrific bread substitute for off-the-shelf multi-grains.

Nutritional Information (Approximate per 1 serving):
Calories: 230 | Total Fat: 18g | Saturated Fat: 3g | Cholesterol: 195mg | Sodium: 290mg | Total Carbs: 12g | Fiber: 5g | Sugars: 2g | Protein: 9g

Beneficial Nutrients & Anti-Inflammatories:

Avocado: Monounsaturated Fats, Vitamin E, Fiber, Phytosterols | Soft Boiled Eggs: Omega-3 Fatty Acids, Choline | Avocado Mayo: Monounsaturated Fats, Vitamin E | Dijon Mustard: Selenium | Green Onions: Quercetin, Sulfur Compounds | Fresh Chives: Allicin, Vitamin K | Black Pepper: Piperine | Sesame Ezekiel Bread: Fiber, Lignans, Whole Grains | Olive Oil: Monounsaturated Fats, Polyphenols | Baby Spinach: Vitamin K, Carotenoids (Beta-Carotene, Lutein, Zeaxanthin), Flavonoids, Vitamin C | Fresh Raspberries: Anthocyanins, Vitamin C, Fiber

Ingredients:

- Avocado, sliced (150g; 1 avocado per slice of bread)
- 12 soft boiled medium eggs (~56g each; 672g total)
- 2/3 cup (153g) avocado mayonnaise (I use Primal Kitchen's avocado mayo)
- 1 tbsp (15g) Dijon mustard
- 1/3 cup (33g) green onions, chopped
- 1/4 cup (13g) fresh chives, chopped

- 1/2 tsp (3g) sea salt
- 1/4 tsp (.58g) black pepper
- 1 slice sesame Ezekiel bread (found in your supermarket's freezer section)
- 1 tbsp (13.3g) olive oil
- 1.5 cups (45g) baby spinach
- 1/2 cup (62.5g) fresh raspberries (on the side)
- Pat of butter for toast (optional)

Directions:

1. Grab a large mixing bowl and set aside.
2. Soft boil the eggs in a large pot, about 6 to 7 minutes. Drain water and cool off eggs by running under cold water for at least 2 minutes.
3. Peel eggs and chop into small chunks. Add to mixing bowl.
4. Add in avocado mayo, mustard, green onions, chives, salt, and pepper. Stir well. I recommend you refrigerate for at least 1 hour before serving.
5. Toast Ezekiel bread, add butter (recommended)
6. Add avocado slices on bread, add spinach, and top everything with egg mixture.

EGG WHITE FRITTATA WITH AVOCADO

Time: 20 minutes
Serving size: 2

High protein, low carb, and plenty of beneficial anti-inflammatory nutrients. It's also simple to make and delicious!

Nutritional Information (Approximate per 1 serving):
Calories: 259 | Protein: 22g | Fat: 15g | Carbs: 8g | Sugars: 2g | Protein: 9g

Beneficial Nutrients & Anti-Inflammatories:

Spinach: Vitamin K, Vitamin C, Flavonoids | Red Bell Pepper: Vitamin C, Beta-carotene, Quercetin | Green Onions: Vitamin K, Quercetin | Cheddar Cheese: Conjugated Linoleic Acid (CLA) | Nutritional Yeast: B Vitamins, Beta-glucan, Antioxidants | Egg Whites: Selenium | Butter/Coconut Oil: Medium-Chain Triglycerides (MCTs) (in coconut oil), Butyrate (in butter) | Italian Seasoning: Various antioxidants and anti-inflammatory compounds from herbs like oregano, basil, and rosemary

Ingredients:

- 1 cup (223g) egg whites (I use Egg Beaters or Bob Evans liquid whites)
- 2 green onions (17g; diced)
- 1 red bell pepper (~160g; diced)
- 1.5 cups (45g) spinach
- 1/2 cup (57g) shredded cheddar cheese (dairy substitute: 1 tbsp (9g) nutritional yeast)
- 1 tbsp (14g) unsalted butter
- 1 tsp (1.8g) Italian seasoning
- .25 tsp (1.5g) kosher salt

Directions:

1. Preheat the oven to broil.
2. Heat a non-stick pan over medium heat, add butter, and sauté red bell pepper for 6-8 minutes.
3. In a separate bowl, beat egg whites, Italian seasoning, salt, and green onion. If using nutritional yeast, add at this stage and mix.
4. Add egg mixture and spinach to pan with red peppers, cook until egg is solid and spinach is wilted.
5. Top with cheese and broil for 2-3 minutes, until cheese and edges are lightly browned.
6. Cut into wedges.
7. Serve with avocado on the side and with your favorite sauce (I like green Tabasco or Tapatilo).

GOLDEN ALMOND & COCONUT MILK

Time: 15 minutes
Serving size: 1 cup (240 ml)

Fragrant, spicy, delicious. This is an anti-inflammatory powerhouse, with turmeric, black pepper, cinnamon, and ginger!

Nutritional Information (Approximate per 1 serving):

Calories: 150 kcal | Protein: 2g | Carbohydrates: 8g |
Dietary Fiber: 2g | Sugars: 6g | Fat: 12g | Saturated Fat: 5g
| Sodium: 100mg

Beneficial Nutrients & Anti-Inflammatories:

Turmeric: Curcumin | Ginger: Gingerol, other antioxidants | Cinnamon: Cinnamaldehyde, antioxidants | Coconut
Milk: Lauric acid, antioxidants | Almond Milk: Vitamin E, healthy fats, antioxidants

....

Ingredients:

- 1 cup (244g; 8.5oz) unsweetened almond milk
- 1 cup (228g; 8oz) coconut milk (canned or fresh)
- 1 teaspoon (2.5g) ground turmeric
- 1/2 teaspoon (1.15g) ground cinnamon
- 1/2 teaspoon (1g) ground ginger

- 1 tablespoon (20g; .7oz) maple syrup (adjust to taste)
- 1/4 teaspoon (.58g) ground black pepper (to enhance curcumin absorption)
- 1/2 teaspoon (3g; .1oz) vanilla extract (optional)
- 1/8 tsp (.71g) sea salt

....

Directions:

Prepare the Golden Milk:

1. In a small saucepan, combine the almond milk and coconut milk. Heat over medium heat until warm, but not boiling.

Add the Spices:

2. Stir in the ground turmeric, ground cinnamon, ground ginger, maple syrup, ground black pepper, vanilla extract (if using), and a pinch of sea salt.
3. Whisk continuously to ensure the spices are well incorporated and the milk is smooth.

Simmer & Cool:

4. Reduce the heat to low and let the mixture simmer for about 5 minutes, whisking occasionally.
5. Remove from heat and let it sit for a minute to allow the flavors to meld.

Serve:

6. Pour the golden almond & coconut milk into mugs.
7. Optionally, garnish with a sprinkle of cinnamon on top.

KETO BREAKFAST STACK

Time: 15 minutes
Serving size:
1 complete stack

Why cook plain old boring eggs in the morning when you can add just a few simple ingredients to boost the nutrient content and flavor? This one is low in unhealthy carbs, high in fiber and, as the title suggests, Keto friendly. I'll admit, the stack has a tough time staying as a stack once everything is done. I normally place everything on a plate and combine them as I eat. It's pretty delish.

Nutritional Information (Approximate per 1 serving):

Calories: 523 | Protein: 15g | Carbs: 16g | Fiber: 9g | Fat: 30g | Sugar: 2g

Beneficial Nutrients & Anti-Inflammatories:

Monounsaturated fats (Avocado, Avocado Oil, Avocado Mayo) | Vitamin E (Avocado, Sesame Seeds) | Carotenoids (Avocado) | Choline (Egg) | Oleic acid (Avocado, Avocado Oil) | Vitamin K (Romaine Lettuce) | Vitamin A (Romaine Lettuce) | Quercetin (Red Onion) | Lycopene (Tomato) | Vitamin C (Tomato) | Whole grains (Ezekiel Bread) | Sesamin (Sesame Seeds)

....

Ingredients:

- 1 avocado, halved (150g)
- 1 fried egg (in avocado oil)
- 2 slices of crisp turkey bacon
- 1 lettuce leaf (I like romaine)
- 1 red onion slice (sliced thin)
- 1 tomato slice (sliced thick)

- 1 tbsp (14g) avocado mayo
- 1 slice sesame Ezekiel bread (optional)
- Salt and pepper to taste
- Sesame seeds for extra crunch (optional)

....

Directions:

1. Start by microwaving the turkey bacon. Lay down a paper towel on a dish, place the bacon strips, and cover with another paper towel. For a 1000 watt microwave, cook for at least 2 minutes. Adjust crispness level in 30 second increments if 2 minutes isn't enough.
2. Fry the egg. I like over-hard, most people like over-easy. Your choice. Season with S&P.
3. Cut avocados in half and remove pit. Fill hole with avocado mayo.
4. Layer with lettuce, tomato, onion, bacon, and egg.
5. Season with sea salt, top with the other half of the avocado, and sprinkle with sesame seeds.
6. I've found that eating this with a slice of Ezekiel bread is delicious. If you're following a keto diet, leave the bread out.

MANGO, KALE & TURMERIC SUPER SMOOTHIE

Time: 10 minutes
Serving size: 2

Loaded with beneficial anti-inflammatory nutrients and fiber. This smoothie is simple to make and can be adjusted based on your tastes. The turmeric and black pepper work together to boost the smoothie's anti-inflammatory impact.

Nutritional Information (Approximate per 1 serving):

(Without added sweeteners) Calories: 410 | Protein: 7g | Carbs: 26g | Fiber: 11g | Fat: 13g | Sugar: 14g

Beneficial Nutrients & Anti-Inflammatories:

Curcumin (turmeric) | Vitamins K, A, C (mango and kale) | Omega-3 fatty acids (chia seeds) | Antioxidants (from mango and kale: beta-carotene, lutein and zeaxanthin, quercetin, flavonoids; Chia seeds: polyphenols) | Fiber

Ingredients:

- 1 cup (140g) fresh or frozen mango chunks
- 1/2 cup (118g) ice cubes (optional, if using fresh mango)
- 1 cup (109g) fresh kale leaves, stems removed
- 1 small ripe banana (80g)
- 1 cup (244g; 8.5oz) unsweetened almond milk (or any non-dairy milk of your choice)

- 1/2 cup (123g) plain yogurt (coconut or cashew milk, low sugar varieties)
- 1 tbsp (10g) chia seeds
- 1 tsp (2.8g) turmeric
- .25 tsp (.58g) black pepper
- 1 tbsp maple syrup (20g) or agave syrup (22g) (optional, for added sweetness)

Directions:

1. **Prepare Ingredients:** Wash the kale leaves thoroughly and remove the stems. Peel the banana and measure out the mango chunks and other ingredients.
2. **Blend:** In a blender, combine the mango chunks, kale leaves, banana, almond milk, yogurt, and chia seeds.
3. **Sweeten:** Add agave or maple syrup if you prefer a sweeter smoothie. I think it's fine without, but your tastes may differ.
4. **Ice (optional):** Add ice cubes if you are using fresh mango and want a colder, thicker smoothie.
5. **Blend Smooth:** Blend on high speed until the mixture is smooth and creamy. If the smoothie is too thick, you can add a bit more almond milk to reach your desired consistency.
6. Serve: Pour the smoothie into a glass and enjoy immediately.

MORNING BURRITOS WITH SALSA VERDE

Time: 40 minutes
Serving size: 4

This is a morning burrito with healthier ingredients than your normal burrito. It's pretty delicious and you can easily alter the cholesterol and sodium levels by making intentional choices with eggs, cheese, and added salt. Can't go wrong here!

Nutritional Information (Approximate per 1 serving):

Calories: 400 | Protein: 20g | Carbs: 35g | Fiber: 7g | Sugars: 4g | Fat: 20g | Saturated Fat: 4g | Cholesterol: 150mg (less if using egg whites) | Sodium: 700mg (less if using less salt)

Beneficial Nutrients & Anti-Inflammatories:

Whole Wheat/Sprouted Grain Tortillas: Higher in fiber and nutrients compared to white flour tortillas; Sweet Potatoes: Rich in vitamins A and C, fiber, and antioxidants; Turmeric and Black Pepper: Anti-inflammatory properties; Olive Oil/Avocado Oil: Healthy fats that support inflammation reduction; Avocado: Contains healthy monounsaturated fats and anti-inflammatory compounds; Plant-Based Sausage: Reduces saturated fat intake and adds plant-based nutrients (if using).

Ingredients:

For the Burritos:

- 4 large sprouted grain tortillas
- 6 large eggs (or substitute with 4 large eggs and 1 cup egg whites (220g; 7.75oz) for reduced cholesterol)
- 1/4 cup (61g; 2oz) unsweetened almond milk or oat milk
- 1 cup (113g) shredded cheese (opt for a plant-based cheese if avoiding dairy)
- 1 cup (138g) cooked and crumbled turkey sausage or a plant-based sausage alternative
- 1 cup (133g) diced sweet potatoes
- 1/2 cup (75g) diced bell peppers (red, yellow, or orange)
- 1/2 cup (26g) diced onions
- 1/4 cup (4.25g) chopped fresh cilantro
- 1 avocado, sliced (150g)
- 1 teaspoon (3.18g) turmeric

- 1/2 teaspoon (1.15g) black pepper (to enhance turmeric absorption)
- 1/2 teaspoon (1.15g) ground cumin
- Salt to taste
- 1 tablespoon (13.3g) olive oil or avocado oil

For the Salsa Verde:

- 1 pound (454g) tomatillos, husked and rinsed
- 1/2 cup (26g) chopped white onion
- 1/4 cup (4.25g) fresh cilantro leaves
- 1 tablespoon (15g; .53oz) fresh lime juice
- 1 teaspoon (6.6g; .23oz) maple syrup
- 1 jalapeño or serrano pepper, stemmed and chopped (remove seeds for less heat)
- Salt to taste

Directions:

Salsa Verde:

1. Preheat your oven to broil.
2. Place the tomatillos on a baking sheet and broil until they are charred and softened, about 5-7 minutes. Turn them halfway through to ensure even charring.
3. Transfer the broiled tomatillos to a blender or food processor. Add the chopped onion, cilantro, lime juice, honey, jalapeño, and salt.
4. Blend until smooth. Taste and adjust seasoning if necessary. Set aside.

Burritos:

5. In a large bowl, whisk together the eggs, milk, turmeric, black pepper, cumin, and salt.
6. Heat a large skillet over medium heat and add olive oil or avocado oil.
7. Add the diced sweet potatoes, bell peppers, and onions to the skillet. Cook until the vegetables are tender and the sweet potatoes are slightly crispy, about 8-10 minutes.
8. Add the cooked turkey sausage or plant-based sausage to the skillet and stir to combine.
9. Pour the egg mixture into the skillet and cook, stirring gently, until the eggs are scrambled and fully cooked.
10. Sprinkle the shredded cheese over the egg mixture and stir until the cheese is melted.
11. Warm the whole wheat or sprouted grain tortillas in the microwave or on a dry skillet until pliable.
12. To assemble the burritos, place a portion of the egg mixture in the center of each tortilla. Top with sliced avocado and chopped cilantro.
13. Roll up the tortillas, folding in the sides as you go, to create a burrito.
14. Serve the burritos with the salsa verde on the side or spooned over the top.

NO-BAKE TURMERIC PROTEIN DONUTS

Time: 65 minutes
Serving size: 8 donuts

You had me at donut. These are really tasty, and you'll definitely want to eat more than one. Just be careful – everything in moderation. Right? Right.

Nutritional Information (Approximate per 1 serving):

Calories: 200 kcal | Protein: 10g | Carbohydrates: 20g | Dietary Fiber: 4g | Sugars: 10g (including honey or maple syrup) | Fat: 10g | Saturated Fat: 1g | Sodium: 50mg

Beneficial Nutrients & Anti-Inflammatories:

Rolled Oats: Fiber, antioxidants | Turmeric: Curcumin | Cinnamon: Cinnamaldehyde, antioxidants | Ginger: Gingerol, antioxidants | Black Pepper: Piperine | Almonds (in almond flour and almond butter): Monounsaturated fats, vitamin E, antioxidants | Walnuts (optional): Omega-3 fatty acids, antioxidants

Ingredients:

- 1 cup (90g) rolled oats (Bob's Red Mill is a recommended brand. They don't use chemicals to process their oats)
- 1/2 cup (284g) vanilla protein powder (plant-based)
- 1/4 cup (24g) almond flour
- 1/4 cup (80g; 2.82oz) maple syrup
- 1/4 cup (60g) almond butter
- 1/4 cup (61g) unsweetened almond milk (or any non-dairy milk of your choice)
- 1 teaspoon (2.8g) ground turmeric

- 1/2 teaspoon (1.15g) ground cinnamon
- 1/2 teaspoon (2.1g) vanilla extract
- 1/4 teaspoon (.5g) ground ginger
- 1/8 teaspoon (.3g) black pepper (enhances turmeric absorption)
- 1/4 cup (30g) chopped walnuts (optional, for topping)
- 1 cup (170g) 70+% dark chocolate chips, for melting

Directions:

1. In a food processor, blend the rolled oats until they form a fine flour.
2. In a large bowl, combine the oat flour, protein powder, almond flour, ground turmeric, ground cinnamon, ground ginger, and black pepper.
3. In a separate bowl, mix together the honey or maple syrup, almond butter, almond milk, and vanilla extract until smooth.
4. Pour the wet ingredients into the dry ingredients and stir until well combined. The mixture should be thick and dough-like.
5. Press the mixture into a donut mold, filling each cavity and smoothing the tops.
6. Sprinkle the chopped walnuts on top of the donuts, pressing them lightly into the dough.
7. Refrigerate the donuts for at least 1 hour to firm up.
8. (optional) Add melted dark chocolate and a sprinkle of turmeric to the top of each (adds to sugar totals).
9. Remove from the molds and enjoy!

NOURISHING TURMERIC SCRAMBLE

Time: 20 minutes
Serving size: 2

This breakfast is an anti-inflammatory powerhouse, loaded with beneficial nutrients and compounds. It also tastes great!

Nutritional Information (Approximate per 1 serving):

Calories: 300 kcal | Protein: 12g | Carbohydrates: 10g | Dietary Fiber: 4g |
Sugars: 2g | Fat: 24g | Saturated Fat: 8g | Sodium: 200mg

Beneficial Nutrients & Anti-Inflammatories:

Turmeric: Curcumin | Coconut Oil: Lauric acid, antioxidants | Kale: Vitamins A, C, K, antioxidants | Black Pepper: Piperine | Ginger: Gingerol, other antioxidants | Avocado (if included): Monounsaturated fats, vitamin E, antioxidants

Ingredients:

- 4 large eggs (200g)
- 1 tablespoon (13.6g; .48oz) coconut oil
- 2 cups (130g) kale, chopped
- 1/2 small onion, finely chopped (~45g)
- 1/2 teaspoon (1.5g) ground turmeric
- 1/4 teaspoon (.6g) ground black pepper
- 1/2 teaspoon (1.1g) ground cumin

- 1/2 teaspoon (1g) ground ginger
- Salt to taste (~.3g)
- Fresh cilantro, chopped (optional, for garnish)
- 1/2 avocado, sliced (~75g; optional, for serving)

Directions:

1. In a medium bowl, whisk the eggs until well combined. Add the ground turmeric, black pepper, ground cumin, ground ginger, and salt. Mix well.
2. Heat the coconut oil in a large skillet over medium heat.
3. Add the chopped onion to the skillet and sauté until it becomes translucent, about 3-4 minutes.
4. Add the chopped kale to the skillet and cook until it begins to wilt, about 2-3 minutes.
5. Pour the egg mixture into the skillet and cook, stirring gently, until the eggs are scrambled and fully cooked.
6. Remove from heat and transfer the scramble to plates.
7. Garnish with fresh cilantro and serve with avocado slices if desired.
8. Enjoy your nutritious and anti-inflammatory meal!

OVERNIGHT OATS WITH BLUEBERRIES & ALMOND BUTTER

Time: 8 hours
Serving size: 1

You really can't beat any overnight oats recipe. They're simple to put together and make a quick breakfast-on-the-go in the morning. As with any oats-based dish, just watch your portion sizing. Moderation, people.

Nutritional Information (Approximate per 1 serving):

Calories: 400 | Protein: 12g | Carbohydrates: 58g | Dietary Fiber: 9g | Sugars: 15g (including added sweetener & blueberries) | Fat: 17g | Saturated Fat: 2g | Sodium: 175mg

Beneficial Nutrients & Anti-Inflammatories:

Blueberries: Anthocyanins, vitamin C | Almonds: Monounsaturated fats, vitamin E, antioxidants | Chia Seeds: Omega-3 fatty acids (alpha-linolenic acid) and fiber | Cinnamon: cinnamaldehyde and other antioxidants | Greek Yogurt: probiotics (live cultures; if included)

Ingredients:

- 1 cup rolled oats (Bob's Red Mill is a recommended brand. They don't use chemicals to process their oats) (80g)
- 1 cup unsweetened almond milk (or any milk of your choice) (240g; 8.1oz)
- 1 cup almond butter (240g)
- 1/2 cup cashew yogurt (120g)
- 1 tablespoon chia seeds (12g)

- 1 tablespoon maple syrup (to taste) (20g; 0.7oz)
- 1/2 teaspoon vanilla extract (2.1g; 0.07oz)
- 1/2 teaspoon ground cinnamon (1.3g)
- 1/2 cup fresh or frozen blueberries (75g)
- 1/4 cup sliced almonds (24g)
- Fresh blueberries and additional almonds for topping (optional, for garnish)

Directions:

1. In a medium-sized bowl or jar, combine the rolled oats, almond milk, yogurt, almond butter, chia seeds, honey or maple syrup, vanilla extract, and ground cinnamon. Stir well to combine.
2. Gently fold in the blueberries and sliced almonds.
3. Cover the bowl or jar with a lid or plastic wrap and refrigerate overnight, or for at least 4 hours.
4. In the morning, give the oats a good stir. If the mixture is too thick, you can add a little more almond milk to reach your desired consistency.
5. Serve the overnight oats in bowls or jars, topped with additional fresh blueberries and sliced almonds if desired.
6. Enjoy your nutritious and delicious breakfast!

PALEO CHOCOLATE-AVOCADO BLUEBERRY MUFFINS

Time: ~30 minutes
Serving size: 9 muffins

This recipe is made with almond and coconut flours. You can also easily regulate the total sugars by varying the amount of dark chocolate chips and coconut sugar. They're pretty delicious (and addictive), I'm not going to lie.

Nutritional Information (Approximate per 1 serving):

Calories: 260 | Carbs: 25g | Protein: 6g | Sugar: 13g | Fat: 17g

Beneficial Nutrients & Anti-Inflammatories:

Avocado: Monounsaturated Fats (Oleic Acid), Vitamin E | Almond Flour: Vitamin E, Magnesium, Fiber | Coconut Flour: Fiber | Dark Chocolate Chips: Flavanols, Magnesium | Blueberries: Anthocyanins, Vitamin C, Fiber | Raw Cacao Powder: Flavanols, Magnesium | Coconut Sugar: Lower Glycemic Index than cane sugar

Ingredients:

- 1 ripe avocado (ripeness is important) (~200g)
- 1 cup almond flour (96g)
- 2 tbsp coconut flour (16g)
- 1/3 cup coconut sugar (53g)
- 2 cups dark chocolate chips (340g)
- ½ cup unsweetened almond milk (120g; 4.1oz)

- 2 large eggs (100g)
- ¼ cup raw cacao powder (24g)
- 2 tsp baking powder (10g)
- ¼ cup fresh blueberries (you can use other types of berries as well) (37g)
- ¼ tsp salt (1.5g)

Directions:

1. Preheat oven to 375 °F. Blend eggs, avocado, sugar, salt, and cocoa powder in a blender.
2. Add dry ingredients, and fold in blueberries and chocolate chips.
3. Transfer the batter to the prepared muffin tray.
4. Bake for 18 minutes or until muffins come out clean.
5. Cool on a wire baking rack.

SAVORY SPICY ANTI-INFLAMMATORY PANCAKES

Time: 15 minutes
Serving size: 4

These are addictive...trust me. And, if you're fun like me, you'll have a little maple syrup for dipping on the side for the savory/sweet effect. Absolutely deeeelish.

Nutritional Information (Approximate per 1 serving):
Calories: 150 kcal | Protein: 6g | Carbohydrates: 18g | Dietary
Fiber: 4g | Sugars: 2g | Fat: 7g | Saturated Fat: 2g | Sodium: 300mg

Beneficial Nutrients & Anti-Inflammatories:
Turmeric: Curcumin | Cumin: Cuminaldehyde, other antioxidants | Ginger: Gingerol, other antioxidants | Black Pepper: Piperine | Spinach/Kale: Vitamins A, C, K, antioxidants | Coconut Oil/Olive Oil: Lauric acid, monounsaturated fats, antioxidants | Carrots: Beta-carotene, antioxidants | Cilantro: Phytonutrients, antioxidants

Ingredients:

- 1 cup chickpea flour (also known as gram flour or besan) (120g)
- 1/2 cup water (adjust to get the right batter consistency) (120g; 4.1oz)
- 1/2 teaspoon ground turmeric (1.5g)
- 1/2 teaspoon ground cumin (1.1g)
- 1/2 teaspoon ground ginger (1g)
- 1/4 teaspoon ground black pepper (enhances turmeric absorption) (0.6g)
- 1/4 teaspoon cayenne pepper (adjust to taste) (0.6g)

- 1/2 teaspoon salt (3g)
- 1 cup chopped spinach or kale (30g)
- 1/4 cup grated carrots (25g)
- 1/4 cup finely chopped onion (40g)
- 1 tablespoon finely chopped fresh cilantro (4g)
- 1 small green chili, finely chopped (optional, for extra heat) (~10g)
  2 tablespoons coconut oil or olive oil for cooking (27.2g; 0.96oz)

Directions:

1. In a large bowl, whisk together the chickpea flour, water, ground turmeric, ground cumin, ground ginger, black pepper, cayenne pepper, and salt until you get a smooth batter. The consistency should be similar to pancake batter; add more water if necessary.
2. Fold in the chopped spinach or kale, grated carrots, chopped onion, fresh cilantro, and green chili (if using).
3. Heat a non-stick skillet or griddle over medium heat and add a bit of coconut oil or olive oil to coat the surface.
4. Pour a ladleful of the batter onto the skillet, spreading it out to form a pancake. Cook for about 2-3 minutes on each side, or until golden brown and cooked through.
5. Repeat with the remaining batter, adding more oil to the skillet as needed.
6. Serve the savory pancakes hot, garnished with additional fresh cilantro if desired.

SMOKED SALMON GRILLED TOFU AVOCADO TOAST

Time: 15 minutes
Serving size: 4

A very tasty combination that has a good amount of fiber. Shoot for sprouted tofu that is high in protein. There are many high-quality tofu brands out there... it's tough to recommend just one. I sought out a local Asian grocery store, but you can also find high quality tofu at your local supermarket.

Nutritional Information (Approximate per 1 serving):

Calories: 340 kcal | Protein: 15g | Carbohydrates: 25g | Dietary Fiber: 7g
| Sugars: 3g | Fat: 19g | Saturated Fat: 2.5g | Sodium: 550mg

Beneficial Nutrients & Anti-Inflammatories:

Avocado: Monounsaturated fats, vitamin E, antioxidants | Olive Oil: Monounsaturated fats, antioxidants | Turmeric: Curcumin | Black Pepper: Piperine | Smoked Salmon: Omega-3 fatty acids (EPA and DHA) | Whole Grain Bread: Fiber, antioxidants | Tofu: Isoflavones, plant-based protein

Ingredients:

- 4 slices of Ezekiel bread (~184g)
- 1 ripe avocado (~200g)
- 4 ounces smoked salmon (113g)
- 4 ounces firm or extra-firm tofu, sliced (113g)
- 1 tablespoon olive oil (13.6g; 0.48oz)
- 1 tablespoon lemon juice (15g; 0.5oz)
- 1/2 teaspoon ground black pepper (0.6g)
- 1/4 teaspoon ground turmeric (1.5g)

- 1/4 teaspoon red pepper flakes (optional) (0.5g)
- Fresh dill or chives for garnish (optional, for garnish)
- Salt to taste (~0.3g)
- 1 tablespoon soy sauce or tamari (optional, for marinating tofu) (18g; 0.63oz)
- 1/2 teaspoon garlic powder (optional, for marinating tofu) (1.6g)

Directions:

1. Prepare the Tofu: If using, marinate the tofu slices in a mixture of soy sauce or tamari and garlic powder for at least 15 minutes.
2. Toast the bread slices until they are golden brown and crisp.
3. While the bread is toasting, heat a grill pan or skillet over medium heat and add the olive oil.
4. Grill or pan-fry the tofu slices for 2-3 minutes on each side, or until they are golden brown and slightly crispy.
5. In a small bowl, mash the avocado with the lemon juice, ground black pepper, ground turmeric, and salt to taste.
6. Spread the mashed avocado mixture evenly over each slice of toasted bread.
7. Layer the grilled tofu slices on top of the avocado.
8. Arrange the smoked salmon slices over the grilled tofu.
9. Sprinkle with red pepper flakes (if using) and garnish with fresh dill or chives.
10. Serve immediately and enjoy!

TOTALLY ADDICTIVE SWEET POTATO CRANBERRY BREAKFAST BARS

Time: 40 minutes
Serving size: 9

Among the addictive recipes in this book, these bars may be at the top. You'll want to eat these all the time. You may even wake up in the middle of the night craving them. I'm sorry ahead of time.

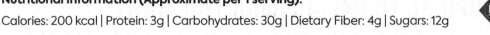

Nutritional Information (Approximate per 1 serving):

Calories: 200 kcal | Protein: 3g | Carbohydrates: 30g | Dietary Fiber: 4g | Sugars: 12g (including honey or maple syrup and dried cranberries) | Fat: 10g | Saturated Fat: 4g | Sodium: 75mg

Beneficial Nutrients & Anti-Inflammatories:

Sweet Potato: Beta-carotene, vitamins A and C | Cranberries: Anthocyanins, vitamin C | Walnuts: Omega-3 fatty acids (alpha-linolenic acid), polyphenols | Chia Seeds: Omega-3 fatty acids (alpha-linolenic acid), fiber | Cinnamon: Cinnamaldehyde, other antioxidants | Ginger: Gingerol, other antioxidants | Turmeric: Curcumin | Black Pepper: Piperine | Coconut Oil: Lauric acid, antioxidants

....

Ingredients:

- 1 cup mashed sweet potato (cooked and mashed) (250g)
- 1 1/2 cups rolled oats (120g)
- 1/2 cup almond flour (48g)
- 1/4 cup maple syrup (to taste) (60g; 2.1oz)
- 1/4 cup coconut oil, melted (54.4g; 1.9oz)
- 1/2 cup dried cranberries (65g)
- 1/4 cup chopped walnuts (30g)
- 1 tablespoon chia seeds (12g)

- 1 teaspoon ground cinnamon (2.6g)
- 1/2 teaspoon ground ginger (1g)
- 1/4 teaspoon ground nutmeg (0.5g)
- 1/4 teaspoon ground turmeric (0.75g)
- 1/4 teaspoon ground black pepper (enhances turmeric absorption) (0.6g)
- 1 teaspoon vanilla extract (4.2g; 0.15oz)
- 1/4 teaspoon salt (1.5g)

....

Directions:

1. Preheat your oven to 350°F (175°C) and line an 8x8-inch baking pan with parchment paper.
2. In a large bowl, combine the mashed sweet potato, honey or maple syrup, melted coconut oil, and vanilla extract. Mix well.
3. In another bowl, whisk together the rolled oats, almond flour, ground cinnamon, ground ginger, ground nutmeg, ground turmeric, black pepper, and salt.
4. Add the dry ingredients to the wet ingredients and mix until well combined.
5. Fold in the dried cranberries, chopped walnuts, and chia seeds.
6. Spread the mixture evenly in the prepared baking pan.
7. Bake for 25–30 minutes, or until the edges are golden and a toothpick inserted into the center comes out clean.
8. Allow the bars to cool completely in the pan before cutting into squares.
9. Store the bars in an airtight container at room temperature for up to 5 days or in the refrigerator for up to 2 weeks.

TROPICAL TURMERIC SMOOTHIE BOWL

Time: 10 minutes
Serving size: 2

Absolutely delicious and packed with anti-inflammatory compounds. I did the best I could to lower the total sugar per serving. I highly recommend the optional monk fruit sweetener if you want this just a touch sweeter.

Nutritional Information (Approximate per 1 serving):

Calories: 250 kcal | Protein: 4g | Carbohydrates: 35g | Dietary Fiber: 8g |
Sugars: 15g (including natural sugars from fruits) | Fat: 10g | Saturated Fat: 6g |
Sodium: 45mg

Beneficial Nutrients & Anti-Inflammatories:

Pineapple: Bromelain, vitamin C | Mango: Vitamins A and C, antioxidants | Banana: Potassium, vitamin C | Coconut
Milk: Lauric acid, antioxidants | Turmeric: Curcumin | Black Pepper: Piperine | Chia Seeds: Omega-3 fatty acids
(alpha-linolenic acid), fiber | Nuts: Omega-3 fatty acids (alpha-linolenic acid), polyphenols

Ingredients:

- 1/2 cup frozen pineapple chunks (85g)
- 1/2 cup frozen mango chunks (83g)
- 1 small banana (~100g)
- 1 cup unsweetened coconut milk (or any milk of your choice) (240g; 8.1oz)
- 1 teaspoon ground turmeric (3g)
- 1/4 teaspoon ground black pepper (enhances turmeric absorption) (0.6g)
- 1 tablespoon chia seeds (12g)
- 1 tablespoon fresh lime juice (15g; 0.5oz)
- 1/2 teaspoon vanilla extract (optional) (2.1g; 0.07oz)

- Stevia or monk fruit sweetener to taste (optional, for added sweetness without sugar) (varies)

Toppings:
- 1/4 cup granola (look for low-sugar or sugar-free options, or use nuts/seeds instead) (30g)
- 2 tablespoons unsweetened shredded coconut (10g)
- 1/4 cup sliced kiwi (42g)
- 1/4 cup fresh berries (such as blueberries or raspberries) (37g)
- 1 tablespoon chopped nuts (such as almonds or walnuts) (7g)

Directions:

1. In a blender, combine the frozen pineapple, frozen mango, banana, coconut milk, ground turmeric, black pepper, chia seeds, fresh lime juice, and vanilla extract (if using).
2. Blend on high speed until smooth and creamy. If the mixture is too thick, add a bit more coconut milk to reach your desired consistency.
3. Taste the smoothie and add stevia or monk fruit sweetener if additional sweetness is desired.
4. Pour the smoothie into a bowl.
5. Top with granola (or nuts/seeds), unsweetened shredded coconut, sliced kiwi, fresh berries, and chopped nuts.

VEGAN BUCKWHEAT BANANA PANCAKES

Time: 20 minutes
Serving size: 2

Say goodbye to sugar-filled, insulin-spiking traditional pancakes. These are hearty, have a good amount of fiber, and are loaded with anti-inflammatory nutrients. They also taste amazing.

Nutritional Information (Approximate per 1 serving):

Calories: 250 kcal | Protein: 5g | Carbohydrates: 45g | Dietary Fiber: 5g | Sugars: 10g | Fat: 6g | Saturated Fat: 1g | Sodium: 200mg

Beneficial Nutrients & Anti-Inflammatories:

Buckwheat: Rutin, quercetin, antioxidants | Banana: Potassium, vitamin C | Chia Seeds: Omega-3 fatty acids (alpha-linolenic acid), fiber | Cinnamon: Cinnamaldehyde, other antioxidants | Almond Milk: Vitamin E, antioxidants

Ingredients:

- 1 cup buckwheat flour (120g)
- 1 tablespoon chia seeds (12g)
- 3 tablespoons water (45g; 1.5oz)
- 1 teaspoon baking powder (5g)
- 1/2 teaspoon baking soda (2.3g)
- 1/2 teaspoon ground cinnamon (1.3g)
- 1/4 teaspoon ground nutmeg (0.5g)
- 1/4 teaspoon salt (1.5g)
- 1 cup unsweetened almond milk (or any plant-based milk of your choice) (240g; 8.1oz)

- 1 tablespoon apple cider vinegar (15g; 0.5oz)
- 1 ripe banana, mashed (~100g)
- 2 tablespoons maple syrup or agave nectar (40g; 1.4oz)
- 1 teaspoon vanilla extract (4.2g; 0.15oz)
- Coconut oil for cooking (as needed, approximately 13.6g per tablespoon; 0.48oz)

Directions:

1. In a small bowl, combine the chia seeds and water. Let sit for about 5-10 minutes to create a chia "egg."
2. In a large bowl, whisk together the buckwheat flour, baking powder, baking soda, ground cinnamon, ground nutmeg, and salt.
3. In another bowl, combine the almond milk and apple cider vinegar. Let sit for a few minutes to create a "buttermilk" effect.
4. Add the mashed banana, maple syrup (or agave nectar), vanilla extract, and chia "egg" to the almond milk mixture. Mix well.
5. Pour the wet ingredients into the dry ingredients and stir until just combined. The batter should be thick but pourable. If it's too thick, add a little more almond milk.
6. Heat a non-stick skillet or griddle over medium heat and add a bit of coconut oil or vegetable oil.
7. Pour 1/4 cup of the batter onto the skillet for each pancake. Cook until bubbles form on the surface, then flip and cook for another 2-3 minutes, until golden brown and cooked through.
8. Repeat with the remaining batter, adding more oil to the skillet as needed.
9. Serve the pancakes warm, with your favorite toppings such as fresh fruit, nuts, or additional maple syrup.

VEGGIE BOMB OMELET

Time: 20 minutes
Serving size: 2

You really cannot go wrong with this recipe. It's absolutely packed with delicious fresh veggies and anti-inflammatory herbs and spices. This one is a go-to in our home...makes the perfect weekend breakfast!

Nutritional Information (Approximate per 1 serving):

Calories: 250 kcal | Protein: 15g | Carbohydrates: 10g | Dietary Fiber: 4g |
Sugars: 4g | Fat: 18g | Saturated Fat: 4g | Sodium: 400mg

Beneficial Nutrients & Anti-Inflammatories:

Turmeric: Curcumin | Black Pepper: Piperine | Cumin: Cuminaldehyde, other antioxidants | Ginger: Gingerol, other antioxidants | Olive Oil/Avocado Oil: Monounsaturated fats, antioxidants | Spinach: Vitamins A, C, K, antioxidants | Bell Pepper: Vitamin C, antioxidants | Onion: Quercetin, antioxidants | Cherry Tomatoes: Lycopene, vitamin C | Avocado: Monounsaturated fats, vitamin E, antioxidants

....

Ingredients:

- 4 large eggs (or 1 cup egg whites for a lighter option) (200g for eggs; 240g for egg whites)
- 1/4 cup unsweetened almond milk (or any milk of your choice) (60g; 2.03oz)
- 1/2 teaspoon ground turmeric (1.5g)
- 1/4 teaspoon ground black pepper (enhances turmeric absorption) (0.6g)
- 1/4 teaspoon ground cumin (1.1g)
- 1/4 teaspoon ground ginger (1g)
- 1/2 teaspoon salt (3g)

- 1 tablespoon olive oil or avocado oil (13.6g; 0.48oz)
- 1/2 small onion, finely chopped (~45g)
- 1/2 red bell pepper, diced (60g)
- 1/2 zucchini, diced (60g)
- 1 cup baby spinach, chopped (30g)
- 1/4 cup cherry tomatoes, halved (37g)
- Fresh cilantro or parsley, chopped (for garnish)
- 1/2 avocado, sliced (for serving, optional) (~75g)

....

Directions:

1. In a medium bowl, whisk together the eggs (or egg whites), almond milk, ground turmeric, black pepper, ground cumin, ground ginger, and salt until well combined.
2. Heat the olive oil or avocado oil in a large non-stick skillet over medium heat.
3. Add the chopped onion, red bell pepper, and zucchini to the skillet. Cook, stirring occasionally, until the vegetables are tender, about 5-7 minutes.
4. Add the chopped spinach and cherry tomatoes to the skillet. Cook until the spinach is wilted, about 2-3 minutes.
5. Pour the egg mixture over the vegetables in the skillet. Cook without stirring until the edges start to set, about 2-3 minutes.
6. Using a spatula, gently lift the edges of the omelet and tilt the skillet to allow the uncooked egg to flow to the edges.
7. Continue cooking until the omelet is fully set and cooked through, about 2-3 more minutes.
8. Carefully fold the omelet in half and slide it onto a plate.
9. Garnish with fresh cilantro or parsley and serve with sliced avocado if desired.

Make a Difference with Your Review

Unlock the Power of Generosity!

"Giving feels good and helps others too." - Someone Wise

People who help others without expecting anything in return often feel happier and live better lives. So, let's try to make a difference together.

I have a question for you...

Would you help someone you've never met, even if you never got credit for it?

Who is this person, you ask? They are like you. They want to be healthier, need some help, and don't know where to start.

My mission is to make anti-inflammatory cooking easy for everyone and to improve overall health. Everything I do is about that mission. And the only way to reach everyone is with *your help*.

Most people decide to read a book based on its cover and its reviews. So here's what I'm asking you to do for a person with inflammation you've never met:

Please help that person by leaving a review for this book.

Your review is free and takes **less than 60 seconds**, but it can change someone's life forever. Your review could help...

...a small business owner serve their community.
...an entrepreneur support their family.
...a person struggling with inflammation and provide the relief they need.
...an unhealthy person to transform their life.
...a dream come true.

To get that 'feel good' feeling and truly help someone, all you have to do is... **leave a review**.

Simply scan the QR code below to leave your review:

scan me to leave a review!

Thank you from the bottom of my heart. Now, back to our regularly scheduled programming.

- Your biggest fan, *Albert*

CHAPTER 4:
DRESSINGS & SALADS

10 GO-TO SALAD DRESSING RECIPES

I've created 10 salad dressing recipes that you can use for all the salads in this book, or you can use them as a dip or sauce for many of the lunch and dinner recipes! They're all delicious and are focused on anti-inflammatory ingredients.

Each one assumes a serving is 2 tablespoons, and each total dressing recipe is for 10 people. All you need to do is combine the ingredients in a blender of your choice. Enjoy!

NOTE: RECIPE NUTRITION INFORMATION IS CALCULATED USING AN INGREDIENT DATABASE (HTTPS://FDC.NAL.USDA.GOV/) AND SHOULD BE CONSIDERED AN ESTIMATE.

LEMON HERB VINAIGRETTE

Time:
Preparation: 5 minutes | Cooking: 0 minutes | Total: 5 minutes

Serving size:
1/2 cup (8 tablespoons)

Nutritional Information (Approximate per 2-tablespoon serving, assuming 4 servings):

Calories: 100 kcal | Protein: 0g | Carbohydrates: 2g | Dietary Fiber: 0g | Sugars: 1g | Fat: 10g | Saturated Fat: 1.5g | Sodium: 150mg

Beneficial Nutrients & Anti-Inflammatories:

Olive Oil: Monounsaturated fats, antioxidants | Lemon: Vitamin C, antioxidants | Garlic: Allicin, antioxidants | Oregano: Anti-inflammatory properties | Parsley: Vitamin C, flavonoids | Honey: Antioxidants (in moderation)

Ingredients:

- 1/4 cup extra-virgin olive oil (54.4g; 1.92oz)
- 2 tablespoons lemon juice (freshly squeezed) (30g; 1.02oz)
- 1 teaspoon lemon zest (2g)
- 1 teaspoon honey or maple syrup (optional, for sweetness) (7g)
- 1 clove garlic, minced (~3g)

- 1 teaspoon Dijon mustard (5g)
- 1 tablespoon fresh parsley, finely chopped (4g)
- 1/2 teaspoon dried oregano (0.5g)
- 1/4 teaspoon salt (1.5g)
- 1/4 teaspoon ground black pepper (0.6g)

Directions:

Prepare the Dressing:

1. In a small bowl or a jar with a tight-fitting lid, combine the extra-virgin olive oil, lemon juice, lemon zest, maple syrup (if using), minced garlic, Dijon mustard, chopped fresh parsley, dried oregano, salt, and ground black pepper.

Mix Well:

2. Whisk the ingredients together until well combined, or secure the lid on the jar and shake vigorously until the dressing is emulsified.

Serve:

3. Drizzle the Lemon Herb Vinaigrette over your favorite salad or use it as a marinade for vegetables or grilled meats.

GINGER MISO DRESSING

Time:
Preparation: 5 minutes | Cooking: 0 minutes | Total: 5 minutes

Serving size:
10 tablespoons (enough for 10 servings)

Nutritional Information (Approximate per 1-tablespoon serving, assuming 10 servings):

Calories: 60 kcal | Protein: 1g | Carbohydrates: 3g | Dietary Fiber: 0g | Sugars: 2g | Fat: 5g | Saturated Fat: 1g | Sodium: 190mg

Beneficial Nutrients & Anti-Inflammatories:

Miso: Probiotics, antioxidants | Ginger: Gingerol, other antioxidants | Olive Oil: Monounsaturated fats, antioxidants | Lemon: Vitamin C, antioxidants | Garlic: Allicin, antioxidants

Ingredients:

- 1/4 cup miso paste (60g)
- 2 tablespoons rice vinegar (30g; 1.02oz)
- 1 tablespoon sesame oil (13.6g; 0.48oz)
- 2 tablespoons olive oil (27.2g; 0.96oz)
- 1 tablespoon grated fresh ginger (6g)
- 1 clove garlic, minced (~3g)
- 1 tablespoon maple syrup (optional, for sweetness) (20g; 0.7oz)
- 2 tablespoons water (to thin, if necessary) (30g; 1.02oz)

Directions:

Prepare the Dressing:

1. In a small bowl, whisk together the miso paste, rice vinegar, sesame oil, olive oil, grated fresh ginger, minced garlic, and maple syrup (if using).
2. Add water, one tablespoon at a time, to reach the desired consistency if the dressing is too thick.

Mix Well:

3. Whisk the ingredients together until well combined and the dressing is smooth.

Serve:

4. Drizzle the Ginger Miso Dressing over your favorite salad or use it as a marinade for vegetables or grilled meats.

AVOCADO LIME CILANTRO DRESSING

Time:
Preparation: 10 minutes | Cooking: 0 minutes | Total: 10 minutes

Serving size:
10 tablespoons (enough for 10 servings)

Nutritional Information (Approximate per 1-tablespoon serving, assuming 10 servings):

Calories: 50 kcal | Protein: 0.5g | Carbohydrates: 2g | Dietary Fiber: 1g | Sugars: 0g | Fat: 4.5g | Saturated Fat: 0.5g | Sodium: 50mg

Beneficial Nutrients & Anti-Inflammatories:

Avocado: Monounsaturated fats, vitamin E, antioxidants | Lime: Vitamin C, antioxidants | Cilantro: Vitamin C, flavonoids | Olive Oil: Monounsaturated fats, antioxidants | Garlic: Allicin, antioxidants

Ingredients:

- 1 ripe avocado (~200g)
- 1/4 cup fresh cilantro, chopped (4g)
- 2 tablespoons lime juice (freshly squeezed) (30g; 1.02oz)
- 1 tablespoon olive oil (13.6g; 0.48oz)
- 1 clove garlic, minced (~3g)

- 1/4 teaspoon ground cumin (1.1g)
- 1/4 teaspoon salt (1.5g)
- 1/4 teaspoon ground black pepper (0.6g)
- 2-3 tablespoons water (to thin, if necessary) (30-45g; 1.02-1.52oz)

Directions:

Prepare the Dressing:

1. In a blender or food processor, combine the ripe avocado, fresh cilantro, lime juice, olive oil, minced garlic, ground cumin, salt, and ground black pepper.
2. Blend until smooth. If the dressing is too thick, add water, one tablespoon at a time, to reach the desired consistency.

Mix Well:

3. Blend the ingredients together until well combined and the dressing is smooth.

Serve:

4. Drizzle the Avocado Lime Cilantro Dressing over your favorite salad or use it as a dip for vegetables.

BLUEBERRY BALSAMIC DRESSING

Time:
Preparation: 10 minutes | Cooking: 0 minutes | Total: 10 minutes

Serving size:
10 tablespoons (enough for 10 servings)

Nutritional Information (Approximate per 1-tablespoon serving, assuming 10 servings):

Calories: 40 kcal | Protein: 0.5g | Carbohydrates: 5g | Dietary Fiber: 1g | Sugars: 3g | Fat: 2g | Saturated Fat: 0.3g | Sodium: 30mg

Beneficial Nutrients & Anti-Inflammatories:

Blueberries: Anthocyanins, vitamin C, antioxidants | Balsamic Vinegar: Polyphenols, antioxidants | Olive Oil: Monounsaturated fats, antioxidants | Garlic: Allicin, antioxidants | Honey: Antioxidants (in moderation)

Ingredients:

- 1/2 cup fresh or frozen blueberries (75g)
- 1/4 cup balsamic vinegar (60g; 2.1oz)
- 2 tablespoons olive oil (27.2g; 0.96oz)
- 1 tablespoon maple syrup (optional, for sweetness) (20g; 0.7oz)

- 1 clove garlic, minced (~3g)
- 1/4 teaspoon salt (1.5g)
- 1/4 teaspoon ground black pepper (0.6g)

Directions:

Prepare the Dressing:

1. In a blender or food processor, combine the blueberries, balsamic vinegar, olive oil, maple syrup, minced garlic, salt, and ground black pepper.
2. Blend until smooth.

Mix Well:

3. Blend the ingredients together until well combined and the dressing is smooth.

Serve:

4. Drizzle the Blueberry Balsamic Dressing over your favorite salad or use it as a marinade for vegetables or grilled meats.

TURMERIC GINGER CITRUS DRESSING

Time:
Preparation: 10 minutes | Cooking: 0 minutes | Total: 10 minutes

Serving size:
10 tablespoons (enough for 10 servings)

Nutritional Information (Approximate per 1-tablespoon serving, assuming 10 servings):

Calories: 45 kcal | Protein: 0.5g | Carbohydrates: 4g | Dietary Fiber: 0g | Sugars: 2g | Fat: 3g | Saturated Fat: 0.5g | Sodium: 50mg

Beneficial Nutrients & Anti-Inflammatories:

Turmeric: Curcumin | Ginger: Gingerol, other antioxidants | Citrus: Vitamin C, antioxidants | Olive Oil: Monounsaturated fats, antioxidants | Garlic: Allicin, antioxidants

Ingredients:

- 1/4 cup extra-virgin olive oil (54.4g; 1.92oz)
- 2 tablespoons orange juice (freshly squeezed) (30g; 1.02oz)
- 1 tablespoon lemon juice (freshly squeezed) (15g; 0.5oz)
- 1 tablespoon apple cider vinegar (15g; 0.5oz)
- 1 teaspoon ground turmeric (3g)
- 1 teaspoon fresh ginger, grated (6g)
- 1 teaspoon maple syrup (optional, for sweetness) (7g)
- 1 clove garlic, minced (~3g)
- 1/4 teaspoon salt (1.5g)
- 1/4 teaspoon ground black pepper (0.6g)

Directions:

Prepare the Dressing:

1. In a small bowl or a jar with a tight-fitting lid, combine the olive oil, orange juice, lemon juice, apple cider vinegar, ground turmeric, grated fresh ginger, maple syrup, minced garlic, salt, and black pepper.

Mix Well:

2. Whisk the ingredients together until well combined, or secure the lid on the jar and shake vigorously until the dressing is emulsified.

Serve:

3. Drizzle the Turmeric Ginger Citrus Dressing over your favorite salad or use it as a marinade for vegetables or grilled meats.

GREEN GODDESS DRESSING

Time:
Preparation: 10 minutes | Cooking: 0 minutes | Total: 10 minutes

Serving size:
10 tablespoons (enough for 10 servings)

Nutritional Information (Approximate per 1-tablespoon serving, assuming 10 servings):

Calories: 60 kcal | Protein: 0.5g | Carbohydrates: 2g | Dietary Fiber: 0.5g | Sugars: 1g | Fat: 5.5g | Saturated Fat: 0.5g | Sodium: 100mg

Beneficial Nutrients & Anti-Inflammatories:

Avocado: Monounsaturated fats, vitamin E, antioxidants | Cilantro: Vitamin C, flavonoids | Parsley: Vitamin C, flavonoids | Lemon: Vitamin C, antioxidants | Olive Oil: Monounsaturated fats, antioxidants | Garlic: Allicin, antioxidants

Ingredients:

- 1 ripe avocado (~200g)
- 1/4 cup fresh cilantro, chopped (4g)
- 1/4 cup fresh parsley, chopped (4g)
- 2 tablespoons lemon juice (freshly squeezed) (30g; 1.02oz)
- 1 tablespoon apple cider vinegar (15g; 0.5oz)
- 2 tablespoons olive oil (27.2g; 0.96oz)

- 1 clove garlic, minced (~3g)
- 1/4 teaspoon salt (1.5g)
- 1/4 teaspoon ground black pepper (0.6g)
- 2-3 tablespoons water (to thin, if necessary) (30-45g; 1.02-1.52oz)

Directions:

Prepare the Dressing:

1. In a blender or food processor, combine the avocado, fresh cilantro, fresh parsley, lemon juice, apple cider vinegar, olive oil, minced garlic, salt, and black pepper.
2. Blend until smooth. If the dressing is too thick, add water, one tablespoon at a time, to reach the desired consistency.

Mix Well:

3. Blend the ingredients together until well combined and the dressing is smooth.

Serve:

4. Drizzle the Green Goddess Dressing over your favorite salad or use it as a dip for vegetables.

SPICY TURMERIC CASHEW DRESSING

Time:
Preparation: 10 minutes | Cooking: 0 minutes | Total: 10 minutes

Serving size:
10 tablespoons (enough for 10 servings)

Nutritional Information (Approximate per 1-tablespoon serving, assuming 10 servings):

Calories: 70 kcal | Protein: 1g | Carbohydrates: 3g | Dietary Fiber: 0.5g | Sugars: 1g | Fat: 6g | Saturated Fat: 1g | Sodium: 100mg

Beneficial Nutrients & Anti-Inflammatories:

Cashews: Healthy fats, antioxidants | Turmeric: Curcumin | Garlic: Allicin, antioxidants | Apple Cider Vinegar: Acetic acid, antioxidants | Olive Oil: Monounsaturated fats, antioxidants

Ingredients:

- 1/2 cup raw cashews (soaked in water for 2 hours and drained) (65g)
- 1/4 cup water (60g; 2.1oz)
- 2 tablespoons olive oil (27.2g; 0.96oz)
- 1 tablespoon apple cider vinegar (15g; 0.5oz)
- 1 tablespoon lemon juice (15g; 0.5oz)
- 1 teaspoon ground turmeric (3g)

- 1 clove garlic, minced (~3g)
- 1/2 teaspoon ground cumin (1.1g)
- 1/4 teaspoon cayenne pepper (adjust to taste) (0.6g)
- 1/4 teaspoon salt (1.5g)
- 1/4 teaspoon ground black pepper (0.6g)

Directions:

Prepare the Dressing:

1. In a blender or food processor, combine the soaked and drained cashews, water, olive oil, apple cider vinegar, lemon juice, ground turmeric, minced garlic, ground cumin, cayenne pepper, salt, and ground black pepper.
2. Blend until smooth and creamy. If the dressing is too thick, add more water, one tablespoon at a time, until the desired consistency is reached.

Mix Well:

3. Blend the ingredients together until well combined and the dressing is smooth.

Serve:

4. Drizzle the Spicy Turmeric Cashew Dressing over your favorite salad or use it as a dip for vegetables.

GARLIC APPLE CIDER VINEGAR DRESSING

Time:
Preparation: 5 minutes | Cooking: 0 minutes | Total: 5 minutes

Serving size:
10 tablespoons (enough for 10 servings)

Nutritional Information (Approximate per 1-tablespoon serving, assuming 10 servings):

Calories: 45 kcal | Protein: 0g | Carbohydrates: 1g | Dietary Fiber: 0g | Sugars: 0.5g | Fat: 4.5g | Saturated Fat: 0.5g | Sodium: 80mg

Beneficial Nutrients & Anti-Inflammatories:

Garlic: Allicin, antioxidants | Apple Cider Vinegar: Acetic acid, antioxidants | Olive Oil: Monounsaturated fats, antioxidants | Honey: Antioxidants (in moderation) | Mustard: Anti-inflammatory properties

Ingredients:

- 1/4 cup apple cider vinegar (60g; 2.1oz)
- 1/4 cup extra-virgin olive oil (54.4g; 1.92oz)
- 2 cloves garlic, minced (~6g)
- 1 teaspoon Dijon mustard (5g)
- 1 teaspoon maple syrup (optional, for sweetness) (7g)

- 1/2 teaspoon salt (3g)
- 1/4 teaspoon ground black pepper (0.6g)

Directions:

Prepare the Dressing:

1. In a small bowl or a jar with a tight-fitting lid, combine the apple cider vinegar, olive oil, minced garlic, Dijon mustard, maple syrup, salt, and ground black pepper.

Mix Well:

2. Whisk the ingredients together until well combined, or secure the lid on the jar and shake vigorously until the dressing is emulsified.

Serve:

3. Drizzle the Garlic Apple Cider Vinegar Dressing over your favorite salad or use it as a marinade for vegetables or grilled meats.

LEMON TURMERIC TAHINI DRESSING

Time:
Preparation: 5 minutes | Cooking: 0 minutes | Total: 5 minutes

Serving size:
10 tablespoons (enough for 10 servings)

Nutritional Information (Approximate per 1-tablespoon serving, assuming 10 servings):

Calories: 60 kcal | Protein: 1.5g | Carbohydrates: 2g | Dietary Fiber: 1g | Sugars: 0.5g | Fat: 5g | Saturated Fat: 0.5g | Sodium: 70mg

Beneficial Nutrients & Anti-Inflammatories:

Turmeric: Curcumin | Lemon: Vitamin C, antioxidants | Tahini: Healthy fats, antioxidants | Olive Oil: Monounsaturated fats, antioxidants | Garlic: Allicin, antioxidants

Ingredients:

- 1/4 cup tahini (60g)
- 2 tablespoons lemon juice (freshly squeezed) (30g; 1.02oz)
- 1 tablespoon olive oil (13.6g; 0.48oz)
- 1 tablespoon water (adjust for desired consistency) (15g; 0.5oz)
- 1 clove garlic, minced (~3g)

- 1 teaspoon ground turmeric (3g)
- 1 teaspoon maple syrup (optional, for sweetness) (7g)
- 1/2 teaspoon ground cumin (1.1g)
- 1/4 teaspoon salt (1.5g)
- 1/4 teaspoon ground black pepper (0.6g)

Directions:

Prepare the Dressing:

1. In a small bowl or a jar with a tight-fitting lid, combine the tahini, lemon juice, olive oil, water, minced garlic, ground turmeric, maple syrup, ground cumin, salt, and ground black pepper.

Mix Well:

2. Whisk the ingredients together until well combined and smooth, or secure the lid on the jar and shake vigorously until the dressing is emulsified. Adjust the consistency by adding more water if needed.

Serve:

3. Drizzle the Lemon Turmeric Tahini Dressing over your favorite salad or use it as a dip for vegetables.

BASIL AVOCADO DRESSING

Time:
Preparation: 10 minutes | Cooking: 0 minutes | Total: 10 minutes

Serving size:
10 tablespoons (enough for 10 servings)

Nutritional Information (Approximate per 1-tablespoon serving, assuming 10 servings):

Calories: 50 kcal | Protein: 1g | Carbohydrates: 2g | Dietary Fiber: 1g | Sugars: 0.5g | Fat: 4.5g | Saturated Fat: 0.5g | Sodium: 50mg

Beneficial Nutrients & Anti-Inflammatories:

Avocado: Monounsaturated fats, vitamin E, antioxidants | Basil: Eucalyptol, antioxidants | Lemon: Vitamin C, antioxidants | Olive Oil: Monounsaturated fats, antioxidants | Garlic: Allicin, antioxidants

Ingredients:

- 1 ripe avocado (~200g)
- 1/4 cup fresh basil leaves, chopped (5g)
- 2 tablespoons lemon juice (freshly squeezed) (30g; 1.02oz)
- 1 tablespoon olive oil (13.6g; 0.48oz)

- 1 clove garlic, minced (~3g)
- 1/4 teaspoon salt (1.5g)
- 1/4 teaspoon ground black pepper (0.6g)
- 2-3 tablespoons water (to thin, if necessary) (30-45g; 1.02-1.52oz)

Directions:

Prepare the Dressing:

1. In a blender or food processor, combine the ripe avocado, fresh basil leaves, lemon juice, olive oil, minced garlic, salt, and black pepper.
2. Blend until smooth. If the dressing is too thick, add water, one tablespoon at a time, to reach the desired consistency.

Mix Well:

3. Blend the ingredients together until well combined and the dressing is smooth.

Serve:

4. Drizzle the Basil Avocado Dressing over your favorite salad or use it as a dip for vegetables.

SPINACH WITH ALMOND-CRUSTED SALMON & LEMON BASIL DRESSING

Time: 30 minutes
Serving size: 4

Fresh spinach, delicious salmon, and an addictive dressing. A great anti-inflammatory combo! You can also use any of the 10 dressings from the salad dressing section of this book.

Nutritional Information (Approximate per 1 serving):

Calories: 550 kcal | Protein: 35g | Carbohydrates: 20g | Dietary Fiber: 8g | Sugars: 8g | Fat: 36g | Saturated Fat: 6g | Sodium: 400mg

Beneficial Nutrients & Anti-Inflammatories:

Spinach: Vitamins A, C, K, antioxidants | Almonds: Monounsaturated fats, vitamin E, antioxidants | Salmon: Omega-3 fatty acids (EPA and DHA) | Olive Oil: Monounsaturated fats, antioxidants | Turmeric: Curcumin | Black Pepper: Piperine | Avocado: Monounsaturated fats, vitamin E, antioxidants | Apple Cider Vinegar: Acetic acid, polyphenols

Ingredients:

For the Salmon:

- 4 salmon fillets (about 6 ounces each) (170g each)
- 1 cup almonds, finely chopped or ground (140g)
- 1/4 cup whole wheat flour (or almond flour for a gluten-free option) (30g for whole wheat flour; 24g for almond flour)
- 2 tablespoons Dijon mustard (30g)
- 1 tablespoon honey or maple syrup (20g; 0.7oz)
- 1 tablespoon olive oil (13.6g; 0.48oz)
- Salt and pepper to taste (~1.5g salt; ~0.6g pepper)

For the Salad:

- 8 cups fresh baby spinach leaves (240g)
- 1 cup cherry tomatoes, halved (150g)
- 1/2 red onion, thinly sliced (~60g)
- 1 avocado, sliced (~200g)
- 1/4 cup dried cranberries (30g)
- 1/4 cup chopped pecans (25g)

For the Lemon Basil Dressing:

- 1/4 cup lemon juice (60g; 2.1oz)
- 1/4 cup olive oil (54.4g; 1.92oz)
- 2 tablespoons fresh basil, finely chopped (10g)
- 1 tablespoon Dijon mustard (15g)
- 1 tablespoon maple syrup (20g; 0.7oz)
- 1 teaspoon lemon zest (2g)
- 1/4 teaspoon ground black pepper (0.6g)
- Salt to taste (~1.5g)

Directions:

Prepare the Salmon:

1. Preheat your oven to 400°F (200°C) and line a baking sheet with parchment paper.
2. In a small bowl, mix the Dijon mustard and maple syrup.
3. In another bowl, combine the chopped almonds, flour, salt, and pepper.
4. Brush each salmon fillet with the mustard mixture, then press into the almond mixture to coat evenly.
5. Heat the olive oil in a large skillet over medium-high heat. Add the salmon fillets and cook for 2-3 minutes on each side, or until the almonds are golden brown.
6. Transfer the salmon fillets to the prepared baking sheet and bake for 10-12 minutes, or until the salmon is cooked through.

Prepare the Dressing:

7. In a small bowl, whisk together the lemon juice, olive oil, chopped fresh basil, Dijon mustard, honey (or maple syrup), lemon zest, ground black pepper, and salt to taste. Set aside.

Assemble the Salad:

8. In a large salad bowl, combine the spinach leaves, cherry tomatoes, red onion, avocado slices, dried cranberries, and chopped pecans.
9. Drizzle the dressing over the salad and toss gently to combine.

Serve:

10. Divide the salad among four plates and top each with a salmon fillet.
11. Serve immediately and enjoy!

AVOCADO TUNA SPINACH SALAD WITH ORANGE GINGER DRESSING

Time: 10 minutes
Serving size: 4

A very refreshing salad. The combination of the fresh tomatoes, parsley (or cilantro) and the orange dressing makes it a great summer salad.

Nutritional Information (Approximate per 1 serving):

Calories: 350 kcal | Protein: 18g | Carbohydrates: 12g | Dietary Fiber: 7g | Sugars: 3g | Fat: 27g | Saturated Fat: 4g | Sodium: 400mg

Beneficial Nutrients & Anti-Inflammatories:

Spinach: Vitamins A, C, K, antioxidants | Avocado: Monounsaturated fats, vitamin E, antioxidants | Tuna: Omega-3 fatty acids (EPA and DHA) | Olive Oil: Monounsaturated fats, antioxidants | Turmeric: Curcumin | Black Pepper: Piperine | Lemon: Vitamin C, antioxidants | Sunflower Seeds: Vitamin E, healthy fats, antioxidants

....

Ingredients:

For the Salad:

- 5 ounces baby spinach leaves (142g)
- 2 ripe avocados, diced (~400g total)
- 2 (5-ounce) cans tuna, drained (preferably packed in water or olive oil) (142g each)
- 1/2 red onion, thinly sliced (~60g)
- 1/2 cup cherry tomatoes, halved (75g)
- 1/4 cup sliced black olives (35g)
- 1/4 cup chopped fresh cilantro or parsley (4g)
- 1/4 cup sunflower seeds (or any other seed/nut of choice for added crunch) (35g)

For the Orange Ginger Dressing:

- 1/4 cup fresh orange juice (60g; 2.1oz)
- 2 tablespoons rice vinegar (30g; 1.02oz)
- 1 tablespoon grated fresh ginger (6g)
- 1 tablespoon maple syrup (20g; 0.7oz)
- 1 tablespoon sesame oil (13.6g; 0.48oz)
- 1 teaspoon soy sauce or tamari (6g; 0.21oz)
- 1/4 teaspoon ground black pepper (0.6g)
- Salt to taste (~1.5g)

....

Directions:

Prepare the Dressing:

1. In a small bowl, whisk together the fresh orange juice, rice vinegar, grated fresh ginger, maple syrup, sesame oil, soy sauce (or tamari), ground black pepper, and salt to taste. Set aside.

Prepare the Salad:

2. In a large salad bowl, combine the baby spinach leaves, diced avocados, drained tuna, sliced red onion, cherry tomatoes, black olives, and chopped cilantro or parsley.
3. Pour the dressing over the salad and toss gently to combine.
4. Sprinkle sunflower seeds (or your choice of seeds/nuts) on top for added crunch.

BREAKFAST SALAD WITH ROASTED SWEET POTATOES & TAHINI CILANTRO DRESSING

Time: 35-40 minutes
Serving size: 4

Salad for breakfast? You betcha. Starting your day off with fresh greens, avocado, sweet potato, berries, and an absolutely delicious dressing will give you the energy you need for the rest of the day. This one is also loaded with anti-inflammatory nutrients.

Nutritional Information (Approximate per 1 serving):

Calories: 400 kcal | Protein: 12g | Carbohydrates: 35g | Dietary Fiber: 9g |
Sugars: 12g | Fat: 24g | Saturated Fat: 4g | Sodium: 250mg

Beneficial Nutrients & Anti-Inflammatories:

Sweet Potatoes: Beta-carotene, vitamins A and C | Spinach: Vitamins A, C, K, antioxidants | Avocado: Monounsaturated fats, vitamin E, antioxidants | Olive Oil: Monounsaturated fats, antioxidants | Tahini: Healthy fats, antioxidants | Cilantro: Phytonutrients, antioxidants | Turmeric: Curcumin | Black Pepper: Piperine | Pumpkin Seeds: Magnesium, zinc, antioxidants

Ingredients:

For the Salad:

- 2 medium sweet potatoes, peeled and diced (~400g total)
- 2 tablespoons olive oil (27.2g; 0.96oz)
- 1 teaspoon ground cumin (3g)
- 1/2 teaspoon paprika (1.2g)
- 1/2 teaspoon garlic powder (1.6g)
- Salt and pepper to taste (~1.5g salt; ~0.6g pepper)
- 5 ounces baby spinach leaves (142g)
- 1 avocado, sliced (~200g)
- 4 hard-boiled eggs, quartered (200g total)
- 1/2 red onion, thinly sliced (~60g)
- 1/4 cup pumpkin seeds (pepitas) (30g)

- 1/4 cup dried cranberries (30g)

For the Tahini Cilantro Dressing:

- 1/4 cup tahini (60g)
- 1/4 cup fresh cilantro, finely chopped (4g)
- 2 tablespoons lemon juice (30g; 1.02oz)
- 1 tablespoon olive oil (13.6g; 0.48oz)
- 1 tablespoon maple syrup (20g; 0.7oz)
- 1 clove garlic, minced (~3g)
- 1/4 cup water (or as needed for desired consistency) (60g; 2.1oz)
- Salt and pepper to taste (~1.5g salt; ~0.6g pepper)

Directions:

Roast the Sweet Potatoes:

1. Preheat your oven to 400°F (200°C) and line a baking sheet with parchment paper.
2. In a large bowl, toss the diced sweet potatoes with olive oil, ground cumin, paprika, garlic powder, salt, and pepper.
3. Spread the sweet potatoes evenly on the prepared baking sheet.
4. Roast for 25-30 minutes, or until tender and slightly crispy, tossing halfway through cooking.

Prepare the Dressing:

5. In a small bowl, whisk together the tahini, fresh cilantro, lemon juice, olive oil, maple syrup, minced garlic, and water. Adjust the water quantity to achieve your desired consistency.
6. Season with salt and pepper to taste. Set aside.

Assemble the Salad:

7. In a large salad bowl, combine the baby spinach leaves, sliced avocado, quartered hard-boiled eggs, thinly sliced red onion, pumpkin seeds, and dried cranberries.
8. Add the roasted sweet potatoes to the salad.

Dress the Salad:

9. Drizzle the Tahini Cilantro Dressing over the salad and toss gently to combine.

BROCCOLI & CAULIFLOWER SALAD WITH HONEY DIJON TURMERIC DRESSING

Time: 15 minutes
Serving size: 4

I tried this recipe both with raw vegetables, and cooked. If you don't care for raw broccoli and cauliflower, I recommend cooking/steaming them ahead of time and chilling until cool. Then add.

Nutritional Information (Approximate per 1 serving):

Calories: 250 kcal | Protein: 6g | Carbohydrates: 24g | Dietary Fiber: 6g |
Sugars: 10g | Fat: 15g | Saturated Fat: 2g | Sodium: 150mg

Beneficial Nutrients & Anti-Inflammatories:

Broccoli: Sulforaphane, vitamins C and K, antioxidants | Cauliflower: Glucosinolates, vitamin C, antioxidants | Olive Oil: Monounsaturated fats, antioxidants | Turmeric: Curcumin | Black Pepper: Piperine | Almonds: Monounsaturated fats, vitamin E, antioxidants | Sunflower Seeds: Vitamin E, healthy fats, antioxidants | Parsley: Vitamin C, flavonoids

Ingredients:

For the Salad:

- 3 cups broccoli florets (270g)
- 3 cups cauliflower florets (300g)
- 1/2 red onion, finely chopped (~60g)
- 1/2 cup dried cranberries (65g)
- 1/4 cup sunflower seeds (35g)
- 1/4 cup sliced almonds (24g)
- 1/4 cup fresh parsley, chopped (4g)

For the Dressing:

- 1/4 cup olive oil (54.4g; 1.92oz)
- 2 tablespoons apple cider vinegar (30g; 1.02oz)
- 1 tablespoon Dijon mustard (15g)
- 1 tablespoon maple syrup (20g; 0.7oz)
- 1 teaspoon ground turmeric (3g)
- 1/4 teaspoon ground black pepper (enhances turmeric absorption) (0.6g)
- Salt to taste (~1.5g)

Directions:

Prepare the Dressing:

1. In a small bowl, whisk together the olive oil, apple cider vinegar, Dijon mustard, maple syrup, ground turmeric, ground black pepper, and salt to taste. Set aside.

Prepare the Salad:

2. In a large bowl, combine the broccoli florets, cauliflower florets, chopped red onion, dried cranberries, sunflower seeds, sliced almonds, and chopped parsley.

Assemble the Salad:

3. Pour the dressing over the salad and toss gently to combine.
4. Allow the salad to sit for at least 15 minutes before serving to let the flavors meld.

CHICKEN & GRAPE SALAD WITH LEMON HERB DRESSING

Time: 15 minutes
Serving size: 4

Grapes are a surprising anti-inflammatory fruit which are packed with beneficial nutrients. The combination in this salad makes for a refreshing and satisfying meal.

Nutritional Information (Approximate per 1 serving):

Calories: 350 kcal | Protein: 25g | Carbohydrates: 15g | Dietary Fiber: 3g | Sugars: 10g | Fat: 22g | Saturated Fat: 3g | Sodium: 300mg

Beneficial Nutrients & Anti-Inflammatories:

Chicken: Lean protein | Grapes: Resveratrol, vitamin C, antioxidants | Olive Oil: Monounsaturated fats, antioxidants | Lemon Juice: Vitamin C, antioxidants | Dill: Antioxidants, flavonoids | Black Pepper: Piperine | Almonds: Monounsaturated fats, vitamin E, antioxidants | Sunflower Seeds: Vitamin E, healthy fats, antioxidants | Parsley: Vitamin C, flavonoids

Ingredients:

For the Salad:

- 2 cups cooked chicken breast, shredded or diced (280g)
- 1 cup red or green grapes, halved (150g)
- 1/2 cup celery, finely chopped (50g)
- 1/4 cup red onion, finely chopped (40g)
- 1/4 cup almonds, sliced or slivered (24g)
- 1/4 cup fresh parsley, chopped (4g)
- 1/4 cup sunflower seeds (optional for extra crunch) (35g)

For the Lemon Herb Dressing:

- 1/4 cup lemon juice (60g; 2.1oz)
- 1/4 cup olive oil (54.4g; 1.92oz)
- 2 tablespoons fresh dill, chopped (5g)
- 1 tablespoon Dijon mustard (15g)
- 1 tablespoon maple syrup (20g; 0.7oz)
- 1 teaspoon lemon zest (2g)
- 1/4 teaspoon ground black pepper (0.6g)
- Salt to taste (~1.5g)

Directions:

Prepare the Dressing:

1. In a small bowl, whisk together the lemon juice, olive oil, chopped fresh dill, Dijon mustard, maple syrup, lemon zest, ground black pepper, and salt to taste. Set aside.

Prepare the Salad:

2. In a large bowl, combine the cooked chicken, halved grapes, chopped celery, chopped red onion, sliced almonds, chopped parsley, and sunflower seeds (if using).

Assemble the Salad:

3. Pour the dressing over the salad and toss gently to combine.
4. (Optional) Allow the salad to sit for 5 minutes before serving to let the flavors meld.

CHICKPEA SALAD WITH BROCCOLI & GOLDEN MILK-POACHED CHICKEN

Time:
Preparation: 10 minutes | Cooking: 20 minutes | Total: 30 minutes

Serving size:
1/4 of the total dish

An anti-inflammatory powerhouse with the golden milk protein and fresh ingredients of the salad. Try experimenting with different proteins if chicken isn't your thing.

Nutritional Information (Approximate per serving, assuming 4 servings):

Calories: 400 kcal | Protein: 25g | Carbohydrates: 30g | Dietary Fiber: 10g | Sugars: 6g | Fat: 20g | Saturated Fat: 5g | Sodium: 450mg

Beneficial Nutrients & Anti-Inflammatories:

Chicken: Lean protein | Chickpeas: Fiber, protein, antioxidants | Broccoli: Sulforaphane, vitamins C and K, antioxidants | Garlic: Allicin, antioxidants | Turmeric: Curcumin | Ginger: Gingerol, other antioxidants | Olive Oil: Monounsaturated fats, antioxidants | Lemon: Vitamin C, antioxidants | Avocado: Monounsaturated fats, vitamin E, antioxidants | Cilantro: Vitamin C, flavonoids | Parsley: Vitamin C, flavonoids

Ingredients:

For the Golden Milk-Poached Chicken:

*   2 boneless, skinless chicken breasts (approximately 280g each)
*   2 cups unsweetened coconut milk (or any other non-dairy milk) (480g; 16.9oz)
*   1 teaspoon ground turmeric (3g)
*   1 teaspoon ground ginger (2g)
*   1 teaspoon ground cumin (3g)
*   1 teaspoon ground coriander (3g)
*   1/2 teaspoon ground black pepper (1.2g)
*   Salt to taste (~3g)

For the Salad:

*   1 can (15 ounces) chickpeas, drained and rinsed (425g)
*   2 cups broccoli florets, steamed and cooled (180g)

*   1/2 red onion, finely chopped (60g)
*   1/2 cup cherry tomatoes, halved (75g)
*   1/4 cup fresh cilantro, chopped (4g)
*   1/4 cup fresh parsley, chopped (4g)
*   1 avocado, diced (200g)

For the Dressing:

*   1/4 cup olive oil (54.4g; 1.92oz)
*   2 tablespoons lemon juice (30g; 1.02oz)
*   1 tablespoon apple cider vinegar (15g; 0.5oz)
*   1 tablespoon tahini (15g)
*   1 clove garlic, minced (3g)
*   Salt and pepper to taste (~1.5g salt; ~0.6g pepper)

Directions:

Poach the Chicken:

1. In a medium saucepan, combine the coconut milk, ground turmeric, ground ginger, ground cumin, ground coriander, ground black pepper, and salt.
2. Add the chicken breasts and bring to a gentle simmer.
3. Poach the chicken for 15-20 minutes, or until cooked through. Remove the chicken from the saucepan and let it cool. Shred the chicken.

Prepare the Dressing:

4. In a small bowl, whisk together the olive oil, lemon juice, apple cider vinegar, tahini, minced garlic, salt, and pepper. Set aside.

Assemble the Salad:

5. In a large bowl, combine the chickpeas, steamed and cooled broccoli florets, chopped red onion, cherry tomatoes, fresh cilantro, fresh parsley, diced avocado, and shredded chicken.
6. Drizzle the dressing over the salad and toss to combine.

THAI CHICKEN SALAD WITH SESAME GINGER DRESSING

Time: 15 minutes
Serving size: 4

Packed full of beneficial anti-inflammatories. Great flavor. You can substitute the chicken for a protein of your choice.

Nutritional Information (Approximate per 1 serving):

Calories: 400 kcal | Protein: 30g | Carbohydrates: 20g | Dietary Fiber: 6g | Sugars: 8g | Fat: 25g | Saturated Fat: 3g | Sodium: 600mg

Beneficial Nutrients & Anti-Inflammatories:

Napa Cabbage: Vitamins C, K, antioxidants | Red Cabbage: Anthocyanins, vitamin C, antioxidants | Carrots: Beta-carotene, vitamin A | Bell Pepper: Vitamin C, antioxidants | Snow Peas: Vitamins C, K, antioxidants | Olive Oil: Monounsaturated fats, antioxidants | Sesame Oil: Healthy fats, antioxidants | Ginger: Gingerol, other antioxidants | Garlic: Allicin, antioxidants | Sesame Seeds: Healthy fats, antioxidants | Cilantro: Phytonutrients, antioxidants | Green Onions: Antioxidants

Ingredients:

For the Salad:

- 4 cups shredded cooked chicken breast (560g)
- 6 cups Napa cabbage, thinly sliced (420g)
- 2 cups red cabbage, thinly sliced (150g)
- 2 large carrots, julienned (150g)
- 1 red bell pepper, thinly sliced (120g)
- 1 cup snow peas, thinly sliced (100g)
- 3 green onions, thinly sliced (30g)
- 1/2 cup fresh cilantro, chopped (8g)
- 1/4 cup sliced almonds (24g)
- 1/4 cup sesame seeds (36g)

For the Sesame Ginger Dressing:

- 1/4 cup olive oil (54.4g; 1.92oz)
- 2 tablespoons sesame oil (27.2g; 0.96oz)
- 1/4 cup rice vinegar (60g; 2.1oz)
- 2 tablespoons soy sauce or tamari (30g; 1.02oz)
- 1 tablespoon maple syrup (20g; 0.7oz)
- 1 tablespoon fresh ginger, grated (6g)
- 2 cloves garlic, minced (6g)
- 1 tablespoon sesame seeds (9g)
- 1/4 teaspoon ground black pepper (0.6g)
- Salt to taste (~1.5g)

Directions:

Prepare the Dressing:

1. In a small bowl, whisk together the olive oil, sesame oil, rice vinegar, soy sauce (or tamari), maple syrup, grated fresh ginger, minced garlic, sesame seeds, ground black pepper, and salt to taste. Set aside.

Prepare the Salad:

2. In a large salad bowl, combine the shredded cooked chicken, Napa cabbage, red cabbage, julienned carrots, red bell pepper, snow peas, green onions, and chopped cilantro.

Assemble the Salad:

3. Drizzle the Sesame Ginger Dressing over the salad and toss gently to combine.
4. Sprinkle sliced almonds and sesame seeds on top for added crunch.

Serve:

5. Divide the salad among four plates and serve immediately.
6. Enjoy your nutritious and delicious Chinese Chicken Salad!

KALE & QUINOA SALAD WITH AVOCADO & MAPLE MUSTARD DRESSING

Time: 45 minutes
Serving size: 4

I've come to really love quinoa – a complex carb that, when eaten in moderation, can really help to moderate insulin levels if used as a replacement for other carbs. The rest of the salad speaks for itself. It's delish.

Nutritional Information (Approximate per 1 serving):

Calories: 400 kcal | Protein: 10g | Carbohydrates: 50g | Dietary Fiber: 10g | Sugars: 10g | Fat: 20g | Saturated Fat: 3g | Sodium: 200mg

Beneficial Nutrients & Anti-Inflammatories:

Quinoa: Fiber, magnesium, antioxidants | Kale: Vitamins A, C, K, antioxidants | Avocado: Monounsaturated fats, vitamin E, antioxidants | Olive Oil: Monounsaturated fats, antioxidants | Pomegranate Seeds: Punicalagins, vitamin C, antioxidants | Butternut Squash: Beta-carotene, vitamins A and C | Pumpkin Seeds: Vitamin E, healthy fats, antioxidants | Cranberries: Anthocyanins, vitamin C | Garlic: Allicin, antioxidants | Parsley: Vitamin C, flavonoids

Ingredients:

For the Salad:

- 1 cup quinoa, rinsed (185g)
- 2 cups water or vegetable broth (480g; 16.9oz)
- 6 cups kale, stems removed and leaves chopped (180g)
- 1 avocado, diced (~200g)
- 1/2 cup pomegranate seeds (87g)
- 1/2 cup roasted butternut squash cubes (68g)
- 1/4 cup pumpkin seeds (pepitas), toasted (35g)
- 1/4 cup dried cranberries (30g)
- 1/2 red onion, thinly sliced (~60g)

- 1/4 cup fresh parsley, chopped (4g)

For the Maple Mustard Dressing:

- 1/4 cup olive oil (54.4g; 1.92oz)
- 2 tablespoons apple cider vinegar (30g; 1.02oz)
- 1 tablespoon Dijon mustard (15g)
- 1 tablespoon maple syrup (20g; 0.7oz)
- 1 clove garlic, minced (~3g)
- 1/4 teaspoon ground black pepper (0.6g)
- Salt to taste (~1.5g)

Directions:

Cook the Quinoa:

1. In a medium saucepan, bring the water or vegetable broth to a boil. Add the rinsed quinoa, reduce heat to low, cover, and simmer for 15 minutes or until the quinoa is cooked and the liquid is absorbed.
2. Remove from heat and let it sit, covered, for 5 minutes. Fluff with a fork and set aside to cool.

Roast the Butternut Squash:

3. Preheat your oven to 400°F (200°C) and line a baking sheet with parchment paper.
4. Spread the butternut squash cubes on the prepared baking sheet, drizzle with a little olive oil, and season with salt and pepper.
5. Roast for 20-25 minutes, or until tender and slightly caramelized. Set aside to cool.

Prepare the Dressing:

6. In a small bowl, whisk together the olive oil, apple cider vinegar, Dijon mustard, maple syrup, minced garlic, ground black pepper, and salt to taste. Set aside.

Massage the Kale:

7. In a large salad bowl, add the chopped kale. Pour half of the Maple Mustard Dressing over the kale and massage the leaves with your hands for about 2-3 minutes. This helps to soften the kale and make it more tender.

Assemble the Salad:

8. Add the cooked quinoa, diced avocado, pomegranate seeds, roasted butternut squash, toasted pumpkin seeds, dried cranberries, thinly sliced red onion, and chopped fresh parsley to the massaged kale.

Dress the Salad:

9. Drizzle the remaining Maple Mustard Dressing over the salad and toss gently to combine.

KALE SALAD WITH COCONUT RANCH DRESSING

Time: 15 minutes
Serving size: 4

You are encouraged to get your hands in there for this one. The treatment of the kale in this salad makes for a more tender kale leaf, and a very satisfying meal.

Nutritional Information (Approximate per 1 serving):

Calories: 300 kcal | Protein: 6g | Carbohydrates: 25g | Dietary Fiber: 8g | Sugars: 10g | Fat: 20g | Saturated Fat: 8g | Sodium: 350mg

Beneficial Nutrients & Anti-Inflammatories:

Kale: Vitamins A, C, K, antioxidants | Coconut Milk/Yogurt: Lauric acid, antioxidants | Olive Oil: Monounsaturated fats, antioxidants | Lemon: Vitamin C, antioxidants | Dill: Flavonoids, antioxidants | Parsley: Vitamin C, flavonoids | Garlic: Allicin, antioxidants | Pumpkin Seeds: Vitamin E, healthy fats, antioxidants | Avocado: Monounsaturated fats, vitamin E, antioxidants

Ingredients:

For the Salad:

- 8 cups kale, stems removed, and leaves chopped (240g)
- 1 cup cherry tomatoes, halved (150g)
- 1/2 red onion, thinly sliced (~60g)
- 1 cucumber, diced (200g)
- 1/2 cup shredded carrots (55g)
- 1/4 cup pumpkin seeds (pepitas) (35g)
- 1/4 cup dried cranberries (30g)
- 1 avocado, diced (~200g)

For the Coconut Ranch Dressing:

- 1/2 cup canned coconut milk (full-fat) (120g; 4.2oz)

- 1/4 cup unsweetened coconut yogurt (or another non-dairy yogurt) (60g)
- 2 tablespoons fresh lemon juice (30g; 1.02oz)
- 1 tablespoon apple cider vinegar (15g; 0.5oz)
- 1 tablespoon olive oil (13.6g; 0.48oz)
- 1 tablespoon fresh dill, finely chopped (3g)
- 1 tablespoon fresh parsley, finely chopped (4g)
- 1 clove garlic, minced (~3g)
- 1 teaspoon onion powder (2.8g)
- 1 teaspoon dried chives (1g)
- 1/2 teaspoon salt (3g)
- 1/4 teaspoon ground black pepper (0.6g)

Directions:

Prepare the Dressing:

1. In a small bowl, whisk together the coconut milk, coconut yogurt, fresh lemon juice, apple cider vinegar, olive oil, chopped fresh dill, chopped fresh parsley, minced garlic, onion powder, dried chives, salt, and ground black pepper. Set aside.

Prepare the Salad:

2. In a large salad bowl, combine the chopped kale, cherry tomatoes, sliced red onion, diced cucumber, shredded carrots, pumpkin seeds, dried cranberries, and diced avocado.

Massage the Kale:

3. Pour half of the Coconut Ranch Dressing over the kale and massage the leaves with your hands for about 2-3 minutes. This helps to soften the kale and make it more tender.

Assemble the Salad:

4. Add the remaining dressing to the salad and toss gently to combine all ingredients.

Serve:

5. Divide the salad among four plates and serve immediately.
6. Enjoy your nutritious and delicious Coconut Ranch Kale Salad!

FARRO & SQUASH SALAD WITH LEMON TAHINI DRESSING

Time: 1 hour 30 minutes
Serving size: 4

A hearty salad packed full of fiber and beneficial nutrients. We really enjoy this one. It's part of our regular salad rotation!

Nutritional Information (Approximate per 1 serving):

Calories: 350 kcal | Protein: 10g | Carbohydrates: 50g | Dietary Fiber: 8g | Sugars: 10g | Fat: 14g | Saturated Fat: 2g | Sodium: 300mg

Beneficial Nutrients & Anti-Inflammatories:

Farro: Fiber, magnesium, antioxidants | Butternut Squash: Beta-carotene, vitamins A and C | Spinach: Vitamins A, C, K, antioxidants | Olive Oil: Monounsaturated fats, antioxidants | Tahini: Healthy fats, antioxidants | Lemon: Vitamin C, antioxidants | Garlic: Allicin, antioxidants | Pumpkin Seeds: Vitamin E, healthy fats, antioxidants | Parsley: Vitamin C, flavonoids | Cranberries: Anthocyanins, vitamin C

Ingredients:

For the Salad:

- 1 cup farro, rinsed (200g)
- 2 cups butternut squash, peeled and diced (272g)
- 2 tablespoons olive oil, divided (27.2g; 0.96oz)
- 1 teaspoon ground cumin (3g)
- Salt and pepper to taste (~1.5g salt; ~0.6g pepper)
- 5 ounces baby spinach leaves (142g)
- 1/2 red onion, thinly sliced (~60g)
- 1/2 cup dried cranberries (65g)
- 1/4 cup pumpkin seeds (pepitas) (35g)
- 1/4 cup chopped fresh parsley (4g)

For the Lemon Tahini Dressing:

- 1/4 cup tahini (60g)
- 2 tablespoons lemon juice (30g; 1.02oz)
- 1 tablespoon olive oil (13.6g; 0.48oz)
- 1 tablespoon maple syrup (20g; 0.7oz)
- 1 clove garlic, minced (~3g)
- 1/4 cup water (or as needed for desired consistency) (60g; 2.1oz)
- Salt and pepper to taste (~1.5g salt; ~0.6g pepper)

Directions:

Cook the Farro:

1. In a medium saucepan, bring 2 1/2 cups of water to a boil. Add the rinsed farro and a pinch of salt.
2. Reduce the heat to low, cover, and simmer for 20-25 minutes, or until the farro is tender but still chewy. Drain any excess water and set aside to cool.

Roast the Squash:

3. Preheat your oven to 400°F (200°C) and line a baking sheet with parchment paper.
4. In a large bowl, toss the diced butternut squash with 1 tablespoon of olive oil, ground cumin, salt, and pepper.
5. Spread the squash evenly on the prepared baking sheet.
6. Roast for 25-30 minutes, or until tender and slightly caramelized, tossing halfway through cooking. Set aside to cool.

Prepare the Dressing:

7. In a small bowl, whisk together the tahini, lemon juice, 1 tablespoon of olive oil, maple syrup, minced garlic, and water. Adjust the water quantity to achieve your desired consistency.
8. Season with salt and pepper to taste. Set aside.

Assemble the Salad:

9. In a large salad bowl, combine the cooked farro, roasted butternut squash, baby spinach leaves, sliced red onion, dried cranberries, pumpkin seeds, and chopped parsley.

Dress the Salad:

10. Drizzle the Lemon Tahini Dressing over the salad and toss gently to combine.

LENTIL KALE SALAD WITH TURMERIC GINGER DRESSING

Time: 30 minutes
Serving size: 4

Loaded with fiber, antioxidants, and a host of anti-inflammatory nutrients. The massaging of the kale in the preparation stage of this salad makes for a more tender leaf and an easier eat. Absolutely delish.

Nutritional Information (Approximate per 1 serving):

Calories: 350 kcal | Protein: 12g | Carbohydrates: 40g | Dietary Fiber: 10g | Sugars: 10g | Fat: 15g | Saturated Fat: 2g | Sodium: 200mg

Beneficial Nutrients & Anti-Inflammatories:

Lentils: Fiber, protein, antioxidants | Kale: Vitamins A, C, K, antioxidants | Olive Oil: Monounsaturated fats, antioxidants | Turmeric: Curcumin | Ginger: Gingerol, other antioxidants | Lemon: Vitamin C, antioxidants | Garlic: Allicin, antioxidants | Pumpkin Seeds: Vitamin E, healthy fats, antioxidants | Dried Cranberries: Anthocyanins, vitamin C

Ingredients:

For the Salad:

- 1 cup green or brown lentils, rinsed (200g)
- 6 cups kale, stems removed and leaves chopped (180g)
- 1 cup cherry tomatoes, halved (150g)
- 1/2 red onion, thinly sliced (~60g)
- 1 carrot, shredded (55g)
- 1/4 cup pumpkin seeds (pepitas) (35g)
- 1/4 cup dried cranberries (30g)

For the Turmeric Ginger Dressing:

- 1/4 cup olive oil (54.4g; 1.92oz)
- 2 tablespoons apple cider vinegar (30g; 1.02oz)
- 1 tablespoon lemon juice (15g; 0.5oz)
- 1 tablespoon fresh ginger, grated (6g)
- 1 teaspoon ground turmeric (3g)
- 1 teaspoon maple syrup (7g)
- 1 clove garlic, minced (~3g)
- 1/4 teaspoon ground black pepper (enhances turmeric absorption) (0.6g)
- Salt to taste (~1.5g)

Directions:

Cook the Lentils:

1. In a medium saucepan, bring 2 1/2 cups of water to a boil. Add the rinsed lentils and a pinch of salt.
2. Reduce the heat to low, cover, and simmer for 20–25 minutes, or until the lentils are tender but not mushy. Drain any excess water and set aside to cool.

Prepare the Dressing:

3. In a small bowl, whisk together the olive oil, apple cider vinegar, lemon juice, grated fresh ginger, ground turmeric, honey (or maple syrup), minced garlic, ground black pepper, and salt to taste. Set aside.

Massage the Kale:

4. In a large salad bowl, add the chopped kale. Pour half of the Turmeric Ginger Dressing over the kale and massage the leaves with your hands for about 2–3 minutes. This helps to soften the kale and make it more tender.

Assemble the Salad:

5. Add the cooked lentils, cherry tomatoes, sliced red onion, shredded carrot, pumpkin seeds, and dried cranberries to the massaged kale.

Dress the Salad:

6. Drizzle the remaining Turmeric Ginger Dressing over the salad and toss gently to combine.

KALE & AVOCADO SALAD WITH BLUEBERRIES, EDAMAME, AND LEMON GINGER DRESSING

Time: 20 minutes
Serving size: 4

If you haven't figured out by now, kale is a superfood that is loaded with beneficial antioxidants and vitamins. Many shy away from kale in favor of other leafs, but I encourage you to give it a try. Massaging the kale leafs during preparation helps in softening them up, and make sure you remove the stems.

Nutritional Information (Approximate per 1 serving):

Calories: 300 kcal | Protein: 8g | Carbohydrates: 20g | Dietary Fiber: 10g | Sugars: 6g | Fat: 22g | Saturated Fat: 3g | Sodium: 150mg

Beneficial Nutrients & Anti-Inflammatories:

Kale: Vitamins A, C, K, antioxidants | Avocado: Monounsaturated fats, vitamin E, antioxidants | Blueberries: Anthocyanins, vitamin C | Edamame: Isoflavones, protein, antioxidants | Olive Oil: Monounsaturated fats, antioxidants | Lemon: Vitamin C, antioxidants | Ginger: Gingerol, other antioxidants | Garlic: Allicin, antioxidants | Sunflower Seeds: Vitamin E, healthy fats, antioxidants | Cilantro: Phytonutrients, antioxidants

Ingredients:

For the Salad:

- 6 cups kale, stems removed and leaves chopped (180g)
- 1 ripe avocado, diced (~200g)
- 1 cup fresh blueberries (150g)
- 1 cup shelled edamame, cooked and cooled (155g)
- 1/2 red onion, thinly sliced (~60g)
- 1/4 cup sunflower seeds (35g)
- 1/4 cup fresh cilantro, chopped (4g)

For the Lemon Ginger Dressing:

- 1/4 cup olive oil (54.4g; 1.92oz)
- 2 tablespoons lemon juice (30g; 1.02oz)
- 1 tablespoon apple cider vinegar (15g; 0.5oz)
- 1 tablespoon fresh ginger, grated (6g)
- 1 teaspoon maple syrup (7g)
- 1 clove garlic, minced (~3g)
- 1/4 teaspoon ground black pepper (0.6g)
- Salt to taste (~1.5g)

Directions:

Prepare the Dressing:

1. In a small bowl, whisk together the olive oil, lemon juice, apple cider vinegar, grated fresh ginger, maple syrup, minced garlic, ground black pepper, and salt to taste. Set aside.

Massage the Kale:

2. In a large salad bowl, add the chopped kale. Pour half of the Lemon Ginger Dressing over the kale and massage the leaves with your hands for about 2-3 minutes. This helps to soften the kale and make it more tender.

Assemble the Salad:

3. Add the diced avocado, fresh blueberries, cooked and cooled edamame, sliced red onion, sunflower seeds, and chopped cilantro to the massaged kale.

Dress the Salad:

4. Drizzle the remaining Lemon Ginger Dressing over the salad and toss gently to combine.

MASHED CHICKPEA SALAD WITH DILL & CAPERS

Time: 10 minutes
Serving size: 4

Hearty and satisfying. Absolutely delicious. Makes for a great side anytime!

Nutritional Information (Approximate per 1 serving):
Calories: 300 kcal | Protein: 9g | Carbohydrates: 25g | Dietary Fiber:
8g | Sugars: 4g | Fat: 20g | Saturated Fat: 3g | Sodium: 400mg

Beneficial Nutrients & Anti-Inflammatories:

Chickpeas: Fiber, protein, antioxidants | Dill: Flavonoids, antioxidants | Capers: Quercetin, antioxidants | Olive Oil: Monounsaturated fats, antioxidants | Lemon: Vitamin C, antioxidants | Garlic: Allicin, antioxidants | Avocado: Monounsaturated fats, vitamin E, antioxidants

Ingredients:

For the Salad:

- 2 cans (15 ounces each) chickpeas, drained and rinsed (850g total)
- 1/4 cup red onion, finely chopped (40g)
- 1 celery stalk, finely chopped (~40g)
- 2 tablespoons capers, drained and chopped (16g)
- 1/4 cup fresh dill, chopped (4g)
- 1 avocado, diced (optional for creaminess) (~200g)
- Salt and pepper to taste (~1.5g salt; ~0.6g pepper)

For the Lemon Dill Dressing:

- 1/4 cup olive oil (54.4g; 1.92oz)
- 3 tablespoons lemon juice (45g; 1.5oz)
- 1 tablespoon Dijon mustard (15g)
- 1 tablespoon maple syrup (20g; 0.7oz)
- 1 clove garlic, minced (~3g)
- 1 tablespoon fresh dill, finely chopped (3g)
- 1 tablespoon caper brine (from the jar of capers) (15g; 0.5oz)
- 1/4 teaspoon ground black pepper (0.6g)
- Salt to taste (~1.5g)

Directions:

Prepare the Dressing:

1. In a small bowl, whisk together the olive oil, lemon juice, Dijon mustard, maple syrup, minced garlic, fresh dill, caper brine, ground black pepper, and salt to taste. Set aside.

Mash the Chickpeas:

2. In a large mixing bowl, add the drained and rinsed chickpeas. Using a potato masher or fork, mash the chickpeas until they are mostly broken down but still have some texture.

Assemble the Salad:

3. Add the finely chopped red onion, chopped celery, chopped capers, fresh dill, and diced avocado (if using) to the mashed chickpeas.
4. Pour the Lemon Dill Dressing over the chickpea mixture and stir well to combine.
5. Season with salt and pepper to taste.

TOFU COBB SALAD WITH AVOCADO HERB DRESSING

Time: 30 minutes
Serving size: 4

Tofu is a wonder protein and is packed with isoflavones. The key is to buy good quality tofu. And the good news is, tofu is not too expensive. According to chefs, the best quality tofu you can readily buy are Hodo Tofu, Visoy Tofu, Whole Foods Organic 365, and Phoenix Bean Tofu. The only one I can personally attest to is the Hodo Tofu, which is delicious and easy to work with.

Nutritional Information (Approximate per 1 serving):

Calories: 400 kcal | Protein: 18g | Carbohydrates: 20g | Dietary Fiber: 8g | Sugars: 5g | Fat: 28g | Saturated Fat: 4g | Sodium: 550mg

Beneficial Nutrients & Anti-Inflammatories:

Tofu: Isoflavones, plant-based protein | Mixed Greens: Vitamins A, C, K, antioxidants | Avocado: Monounsaturated fats, vitamin E, antioxidants | Olive Oil: Monounsaturated fats, antioxidants | Lemon: Vitamin C, antioxidants | Garlic: Allicin, antioxidants | Sunflower Seeds/Pumpkin Seeds: Vitamin E, healthy fats, antioxidants | Chives: Vitamins A, C, K, antioxidants | Cherry Tomatoes: Lycopene, vitamin C | Herbs (Parsley, Dill, Chives): Flavonoids, antioxidants

Ingredients:

For the Salad:

- 4 cups mixed greens (such as romaine, arugula, and spinach) (120g)
- 2 cups firm tofu, diced and lightly pan-fried (340g)
- 4 hard-boiled eggs, quartered (optional for a vegan version) (200g total)
- 1 avocado, diced (~200g)
- 1 cup cherry tomatoes, halved (150g)
- 1/2 red onion, thinly sliced (~60g)
- 1/2 cup cooked and crumbled tempeh bacon or vegan bacon bits (optional) (50g)
- 1/2 cup dairy-free cheese crumbles (such as almond-based or cashew-based cheese) (60g)
- 1/4 cup sunflower seeds or pumpkin seeds (35g)
- 1/4 cup fresh chives, chopped (10g)

For the Avocado Herb Dressing:

- 1 ripe avocado (~200g)
- 1/4 cup fresh parsley, chopped (4g)
- 2 tablespoons fresh dill, chopped (3g)
- 2 tablespoons fresh chives, chopped (5g)
- 1/4 cup lemon juice (60g; 2.1oz)
- 1/4 cup olive oil (54.4g; 1.92oz)
- 2 tablespoons water (or as needed for desired consistency) (30g; 1.02oz)
- 1 clove garlic, minced (~3g)
- 1/4 teaspoon ground black pepper (0.6g)
- Salt to taste (~1.5g)

Directions:

Prepare the Tofu:

1. Drain and press the tofu to remove excess moisture. Dice the tofu into small cubes.
2. Heat a non-stick skillet over medium heat and lightly pan-fry the tofu cubes until golden brown on all sides. Set aside to cool.

Prepare the Dressing:

3. In a blender or food processor, combine the ripe avocado, fresh parsley, fresh dill, fresh chives, lemon juice, olive oil, water, minced garlic, ground black pepper, and salt to taste.
4. Blend until smooth and creamy, adding more water if needed to reach your desired consistency. Set aside.

Prepare the Salad:

5. In a large salad bowl, combine the mixed greens, pan-fried tofu, quartered hard-boiled eggs (if using), diced avocado, cherry tomatoes, thinly sliced red onion, crumbled tempeh bacon or vegan bacon bits (if using), and dairy-free cheese crumbles.

Assemble the Salad:

6. Pour the Avocado Herb Dressing over the salad and toss gently to combine.
7. Sprinkle sunflower seeds or pumpkin seeds and chopped fresh chives on top.

SPINACH & SWEET POTATO SALAD WITH BALSAMIC FIG DRESSING

Time: 40 minutes
Serving size: 4

I'm sure you've seen a version of this salad at any upscale restaurant. That's because the flavors work really well together. I've intentionally left cheese off my salad recipes because dairy tends to cause inflammatory reactions in the body. However, you would typically see a goat cheese with this salad. My advice? Experiment with non-dairy cheeses and see which one you like!

Nutritional Information (Approximate per 1 serving):

Calories: 300 kcal | Protein: 5g | Carbohydrates: 45g | Dietary Fiber: 7g |
Sugars: 15g | Fat: 20g | Saturated Fat: 3g | Sodium: 250mg

Beneficial Nutrients & Anti-Inflammatories:

Spinach: Vitamins A, C, K, antioxidants | Figs: Fiber, antioxidants, vitamins A and K | Olive Oil: Monounsaturated fats, antioxidants | Walnuts: Omega-3 fatty acids (alpha-linolenic acid), polyphenols | Avocado: Monounsaturated fats, vitamin E, antioxidants | Garlic: Allicin, antioxidants | Cranberries: Anthocyanins, vitamin C

. . . .

Ingredients:

For the Salad:

- 6 cups baby spinach leaves (180g)
- 1 large sweet potato, diced (~200g)
- 1 cup olive or avocado oil (for cooking the sweet potato) (216g; 7.6oz)
- 1 cup fresh figs, quartered (150g)
- 1/2 red onion, thinly sliced (~60g)
- 1/2 cup walnuts, toasted (60g)
- 1/4 cup crumbled dairy-free feta cheese (optional) (35g)
- 1/4 cup dried cranberries (30g)
- 1 avocado, sliced (~200g)

- 1 tablespoon paprika (6.9g)

For the Balsamic Fig Dressing:

- 1/4 cup balsamic vinegar (60g; 2.1oz)
- 1/4 cup extra-virgin olive oil (54.4g; 1.92oz)
- 1 tablespoon Dijon mustard (15g)
- 1 tablespoon maple syrup (20g; 0.7oz)
- 1 clove garlic, minced (~3g)
- 2 fresh figs, mashed (30g)
- 1/4 teaspoon salt (1.5g)
- 1/4 teaspoon ground black pepper (0.6g)

. . . .

Directions:

Prepare the Dressing:

1. In a small bowl, whisk together the balsamic vinegar, extra-virgin olive oil, Dijon mustard, maple syrup, minced garlic, mashed fresh figs, salt, and ground black pepper until well combined. Set aside.

Prepare the Sweet Potato:

2. Heat your oven to 430 degrees Fahrenheit. Dice the sweet potato. Add to mixing bowl and drizzle with oilive or avocado oil. Add paprika and toss until coated. Spread potatoes on baking sheet and bake for 25-30 minutes, until lightly browned.

Prepare the Salad:

3. In a large salad bowl, combine the baby spinach leaves, quartered fresh figs, thinly sliced red onion, toasted walnuts, crumbled dairy-free feta cheese (if using), dried cranberries, and sliced avocado.

Assemble the Salad:

4. Add sweet potatoes to top of greens. Drizzle the Balsamic Fig Dressing over the salad.

Serve:

5. Divide the salad among four plates and serve immediately.

STRAWBERRY SALAD WITH TOFU & LEMON MINT DRESSING

Time: 25 minutes
Serving size: 4

Strawberries, lemon, and mint? What a combo! We typically use spinach as the foundation for this salad, but you can use what you like!

Nutritional Information (Approximate per 1 serving):

Calories: 350 kcal | Protein: 12g | Carbohydrates: 20g | Dietary Fiber: 5g | Sugars: 13g | Fat: 25g | Saturated Fat: 3g | Sodium: 300mg

Beneficial Nutrients & Anti-Inflammatories:

Mixed Greens: Vitamins A, C, K, antioxidants | Strawberries: Vitamin C, antioxidants, anti-inflammatory compounds | Tofu: Isoflavones, plant-based protein | Olive Oil: Monounsaturated fats, antioxidants | Mint: Antioxidants, anti-inflammatory compounds | Almonds: Vitamin E, healthy fats, antioxidants | Garlic: Allicin, antioxidants

Ingredients:

For the Salad:

- 4 cups mixed greens (such as arugula, spinach, and romaine) (120g)
- 1 cup strawberries, hulled and sliced (150g)
- 1 block (14 ounces) firm tofu, drained, pressed, and cubed (396g)
- (optional) 1/2 cup vegan cheese crumbles (such as almond-based or cashew-based feta) (60g)
- 1/4 cup fresh mint leaves, chopped (10g)
- 1/4 cup sliced almonds, toasted (24g)
- 1/2 red onion, thinly sliced (~60g)

For the Lemon Mint Dressing:

- 1/4 cup olive oil (54.4g; 1.92oz)
- 2 tablespoons lemon juice (30g; 1.02oz)
- 1 tablespoon apple cider vinegar (15g; 0.5oz)
- 1 tablespoon maple syrup or agave nectar (20g; 0.7oz)
- 1 tablespoon fresh mint, finely chopped (3g)
- 1 teaspoon Dijon mustard (5g)
- 1 clove garlic, minced (~3g)
- Salt and pepper to taste (~1.5g salt; ~0.6g pepper)

Directions:

Prepare the Tofu:

1. Drain and press the tofu to remove excess moisture. Cut the tofu into small cubes.
2. Heat a non-stick skillet over medium heat and lightly pan-fry the tofu cubes until golden brown on all sides. Set aside to cool.

Prepare the Dressing:

3. In a small bowl, whisk together the olive oil, lemon juice, apple cider vinegar, maple syrup (or agave nectar), finely chopped mint, Dijon mustard, minced garlic, salt, and pepper. Set aside.

Prepare the Salad:

4. In a large salad bowl, combine the mixed greens, sliced strawberries, cubed tofu, vegan cheese crumbles, chopped fresh mint, toasted sliced almonds, and thinly sliced red onion.

Assemble the Salad:

5. Drizzle the Lemon Mint Dressing over the salad and toss gently to combine.

Serve:

6. Divide the salad among four plates and serve immediately.

VEGAN STRAWBERRY TOMATO CAPRESE SALAD

Time: 15 minutes
Serving size: 4

It's a caprese salad with strawberries and vegan cheese. Wish you had thought of that, hm? The vegan cheese is really good, which surprised me at first. Nowadays, it's a staple here at the homestead.

Nutritional Information (Approximate per 1 serving):

Calories: 200 kcal | Protein: 5g | Carbohydrates: 15g | Dietary Fiber: 3g | Sugars: 13g | Fat: 14g | Saturated Fat: 2g | Sodium: 200mg

Beneficial Nutrients & Anti-Inflammatories:

Tomatoes: Lycopene, vitamin C | Strawberries: Vitamin C, antioxidants, anti-inflammatory compounds | Basil: Eucalyptol, antioxidants | Olive Oil: Monounsaturated fats, antioxidants | Balsamic Glaze: Polyphenols

----

Ingredients:

For the Salad:

- 2 cups cherry tomatoes, halved (300g)
- 2 cups fresh strawberries, hulled and halved (300g)
- 1 cup fresh basil leaves (20g)
- 1 cup vegan mozzarella balls or slices (such as almond-based or cashew-based mozzarella) (120g)

- 1/4 cup balsamic glaze (60g; 2.1oz)
- 2 tablespoons extra-virgin olive oil (27.2g; 0.96oz)
- **Salt and pepper to taste (~1.5g salt; ~0.6g pepper)**

Directions:

Prepare the Ingredients:

1. Halve the cherry tomatoes and strawberries.
2. If using vegan mozzarella slices, cut them into bite-sized pieces.

Assemble the Salad:

3. On a large serving platter or in a salad bowl, arrange the halved cherry tomatoes, halved strawberries, and vegan mozzarella.
4. Tuck the fresh basil leaves among the tomatoes, strawberries, and mozzarella.

Dress the Salad:

5. Drizzle the extra-virgin olive oil over the salad.
6. Drizzle the balsamic glaze over the top.
7. Season with salt and pepper to taste.

TUNA & OLIVE SPINACH SALAD WITH LEMON CAPER DRESSING

Time: 15 minutes
Serving size: 4

Fresh and tangy. The olives add a bite, plus a dose of antioxidants and monounsaturated fat (healthy fat). You can easily adjust the olive amount to regulate the sodium content of this recipe.

Nutritional Information (Approximate per 1 serving):

Calories: 350 kcal | Protein: 20g | Carbohydrates: 12g | Dietary Fiber: 6g | Sugars: 3g | Fat: 25g | Saturated Fat: 3.5g | Sodium: 600mg

Beneficial Nutrients & Anti-Inflammatories:

Spinach: Vitamins A, C, K, antioxidants | Tuna: Omega-3 fatty acids (EPA and DHA) | Olive Oil: Monounsaturated fats, antioxidants | Olives: Monounsaturated fats, antioxidants | Lemon: Vitamin C, antioxidants | Garlic: Allicin, antioxidants | Sunflower Seeds/Pumpkin Seeds: Vitamin E, healthy fats, antioxidants | Cherry Tomatoes: Lycopene, vitamin C | Parsley: Vitamin C, flavonoids

Ingredients:

For the Salad:

- 6 cups baby spinach leaves (180g)
- 2 (5-ounce) cans tuna, drained (preferably packed in water or olive oil) (284g total)
- 1/2 cup Kalamata olives, pitted and halved (70g)
- 1/2 red onion, thinly sliced (~60g)
- 1 cup cherry tomatoes, halved (150g)
- 1 avocado, diced (~200g)
- 1/4 cup sunflower seeds or pumpkin seeds (35g)

- 1/4 cup fresh parsley, chopped (4g)

For the Lemon Caper Dressing:

- 1/4 cup extra-virgin olive oil (54.4g; 1.92oz)
- 2 tablespoons lemon juice (30g; 1.02oz)
- 1 tablespoon capers, rinsed and chopped (15g)
- 1 teaspoon Dijon mustard (5g)
- 1 clove garlic, minced (~3g)
- 1/4 teaspoon ground black pepper (0.6g)
- Salt to taste (~1.5g)

Directions:

Prepare the Dressing:

1. In a small bowl, whisk together the extra-virgin olive oil, lemon juice, chopped capers, Dijon mustard, minced garlic, ground black pepper, and salt to taste. Set aside.

Prepare the Salad:

2. In a large salad bowl, combine the baby spinach leaves, drained tuna, halved Kalamata olives, thinly sliced red onion, halved cherry tomatoes, diced avocado, sunflower seeds or pumpkin seeds, and chopped fresh parsley.

Dress the Salad:

3. Drizzle the Lemon Caper Dressing over the salad and toss gently to combine.

Serve:

4. Divide the salad among four plates and serve immediately.

TURMERIC SHRIMP SPINACH SALAD WITH LEMON TAHINI DRESSING

Time: 20 minutes
Serving size: 1

This one is a complete meal with healthy protein, fats, and loaded with anti-inflammatories. It also tastes amazing.

Nutritional Information (Approximate per 1 serving):

Calories: 350 kcal | Protein: 25g | Carbohydrates: 10g | Dietary Fiber: 5g | Sugars: 2g | Fat: 23g | Saturated Fat: 3g | Sodium: 600mg

Beneficial Nutrients & Anti-Inflammatories:

Spinach: Vitamins A, C, K, antioxidants | Shrimp: Lean protein, selenium, antioxidants | Olive Oil: Monounsaturated fats, antioxidants | Turmeric: Curcumin | Black Pepper: Piperine | Garlic: Allicin, antioxidants | Almonds: Vitamin E, healthy fats, antioxidants | Lemon: Vitamin C, antioxidants | Tahini: Healthy fats, antioxidants | Cilantro: Phytonutrients, antioxidants | Cherry Tomatoes: Lycopene, vitamin C

Ingredients:

For the Salad:

- 6 cups baby spinach leaves (180g)
- 1 pound large shrimp, peeled and deveined (454g)
- 1 tablespoon olive oil (13.6g; 0.48oz)
- 1 teaspoon ground turmeric (3g)
- 1/2 teaspoon black pepper (1.2g)
- 1/2 teaspoon garlic powder (1.6g)
- 1/2 teaspoon paprika (1.2g)
- 1/2 teaspoon salt (3g)
- 1/2 red onion, thinly sliced (~60g)
- 1 cup cherry tomatoes, halved (150g)
- 1 avocado, diced (~200g)

- 1/4 cup sliced almonds, toasted (24g)
- 1/4 cup fresh cilantro, chopped (4g)

For the Lemon Tahini Dressing:

- 1/4 cup tahini (60g)
- 2 tablespoons lemon juice (30g; 1.02oz)
- 1 tablespoon olive oil (13.6g; 0.48oz)
- 1 tablespoon water (or as needed for desired consistency) (15g; 0.5oz)
- 1 clove garlic, minced (~3g)
- 1/4 teaspoon ground black pepper (0.6g)
- Salt to taste (~1.5g)

Directions:

Prepare the Shrimp:

1. In a medium bowl, combine the shrimp, olive oil, ground turmeric, black pepper, garlic powder, paprika, and salt. Toss to coat the shrimp evenly.
2. Heat a large skillet over medium-high heat. Add the seasoned shrimp and cook for 2-3 minutes per side, or until the shrimp are opaque and cooked through. Remove from heat and set aside.

Prepare the Dressing:

3. In a small bowl, whisk together the tahini, lemon juice, olive oil, water, minced garlic, ground black pepper, and salt to taste. Adjust the water quantity to achieve your desired consistency. Set aside.

Prepare the Salad:

4. In a large salad bowl, combine the baby spinach leaves, thinly sliced red onion, halved cherry tomatoes, diced avocado, toasted sliced almonds, and chopped fresh cilantro.

Assemble the Salad:

5. Add the cooked shrimp to the salad.
6. Drizzle the Lemon Tahini Dressing over the salad and toss gently to combine.

CHAPTER 5:
SOUPS & STEWS

A CLOSE SECOND TO YOUR NANA'S LENTIL SOUP

Time: 40 minutes
Serving size: 6

I'm not going to claim this soup is better than your nana's. I'm not that dumb. Hers is better. But this one is close.

Nutritional Information (Approximate per 1 serving):

Calories: 250 kcal | Protein: 12g | Carbohydrates: 40g | Dietary Fiber: 12g |
Sugars: 8g | Fat: 6g | Saturated Fat: 1g | Sodium: 400mg

Beneficial Nutrients & Anti-Inflammatories:

Onion: Quercetin, antioxidants | Garlic: Allicin, antioxidants | Carrots: Beta-carotene, vitamin A | Celery: Apigenin, antioxidants | Red Bell Pepper: Vitamin C, antioxidants | Lentils: Fiber, protein, antioxidants | Tomatoes: Lycopene, vitamin C | Spinach/Kale: Vitamins A, C, K, antioxidants | Olive Oil: Monounsaturated fats, antioxidants | Parsley: Vitamin C, flavonoids | Lemon: Vitamin C, antioxidants

Ingredients:

For the Soup:

- 2 tablespoons olive oil (27.2g; 0.96oz)
- 1 large onion, diced (~200g)
- 3 cloves garlic, minced (~9g)
- 3 carrots, sliced (180g)
- 2 celery stalks, sliced (~80g)
- 1 large potato, peeled and diced (~300g)
- 1 red bell pepper, diced (~120g)
- 1 cup dried green or brown lentils, rinsed and drained (200g)
- 1 can (14 ounces) diced tomatoes (400g)
- 6 cups vegetable broth (1440g; 50.7oz)
- 1 teaspoon ground cumin (3g)
- 1 teaspoon dried thyme (1g)
- 1 teaspoon dried oregano (1g)
- 1 teaspoon paprika (2.3g)
- 1 bay leaf (~0.2g)
- 1/4 teaspoon ground black pepper (0.6g)
- Salt to taste (~1.5g)
- 2 cups spinach or kale, chopped (60g for spinach; 130g for kale)
- 1/4 cup fresh parsley, chopped (4g)
- 2 tablespoons fresh lemon juice (optional) (30g; 1.02oz)

Directions:

Prepare the Soup Base:

1. In a large pot, heat the olive oil over medium heat.
2. Add the diced onion and sauté until translucent, about 5 minutes.
3. Add the minced garlic and cook for another minute until fragrant.

Add the Vegetables and Lentils:

4. Add the sliced carrots, celery, diced potato, and red bell pepper to the pot.
5. Stir in the rinsed lentils, diced tomatoes (with their juice), and vegetable broth.

Add the Spices:

6. Stir in the ground cumin, dried thyme, dried oregano, paprika, bay leaf, ground black pepper, and salt to taste.
7. Bring the mixture to a boil, then reduce the heat to low and let it simmer for 30-35 minutes, or until the lentils and vegetables are tender.

Add the Greens:

8. Stir in the chopped spinach or kale and cook for another 5-7 minutes, or until the greens are wilted.

Finish the Soup:

9. Stir in the chopped fresh parsley and lemon juice (if using).
10. Taste and adjust the seasoning with additional salt and pepper if needed.

EAT-THE-RAINBOW VEGETABLE SOUP

Time: 35 minutes
Serving size: 6

I mean...it's a vege soup. It's packed with all the good anti-inflammatories the world has to offer. Eat plentifully.

Nutritional Information (Approximate per 1 serving):

Calories: 150 kcal | Protein: 4g | Carbohydrates: 25g | Dietary Fiber: 7g | Sugars: 10g | Fat: 5g | Saturated Fat: 1g | Sodium: 400mg

Beneficial Nutrients & Anti-Inflammatories:

Onion: Quercetin, antioxidants | Garlic: Allicin, antioxidants | Carrots: Beta-carotene, vitamin A | Celery: Apigenin, antioxidants | Bell Peppers: Vitamin C, antioxidants | Zucchini: Vitamin C, manganese, antioxidants | Butternut Squash: Beta-carotene, vitamins A and C | Broccoli: Sulforaphane, vitamins C and K, antioxidants | Purple Cabbage: Anthocyanins, vitamin C, antioxidants | Tomatoes: Lycopene, vitamin C | Kale: Vitamins A, C, K, antioxidants | Turmeric: Curcumin | Olive Oil: Monounsaturated fats, antioxidants | Parsley: Vitamin C, flavonoids | Basil: Eucalyptol, antioxidants

Ingredients:

For the Soup:

- 2 tablespoons olive oil (27.2g; 0.96oz)
- 1 large onion, diced (~200g)
- 3 cloves garlic, minced (~9g)
- 2 carrots, sliced (180g)
- 2 celery stalks, sliced (~80g)
- 1 red bell pepper, diced (~120g)
- 1 yellow bell pepper, diced (~120g)
- 1 zucchini, diced (~200g)
- 1 cup butternut squash, peeled and diced (136g)
- 1 cup broccoli florets (90g)
- 1 cup purple cabbage, chopped (70g)
- 1 can (15 ounces) diced tomatoes (425g)

- 6 cups vegetable broth (1440g; 50.7oz)
- 1 teaspoon ground turmeric (3g)
- 1 teaspoon ground cumin (3g)
- 1 teaspoon dried thyme (1g)
- 1 teaspoon dried oregano (1g)
- 1/4 teaspoon ground black pepper (0.6g)
- Salt to taste (~1.5g)
- 1 cup kale, chopped (30g)
- 1/4 cup fresh parsley, chopped (4g)
- 1/4 cup fresh basil, chopped (optional) (5g)
- 1 tablespoon lemon juice (optional) (15g; 0.5oz)

Directions:

Prepare the Vegetables:
1. Wash and prepare all the vegetables as described in the ingredients list.

Sauté the Aromatics:
2. In a large pot, heat the olive oil over medium heat.
3. Add the diced onion and sauté until translucent, about 5 minutes.
4. Add the minced garlic and cook for another minute until fragrant.

Add the Vegetables:
5. Add the carrots, celery, red bell pepper, yellow bell pepper, zucchini, and butternut squash to the pot.
6. Cook for about 5-7 minutes, stirring occasionally.

Add the Broth and Spices:
7. Pour in the vegetable broth and add the diced tomatoes (with their juice), ground turmeric, ground cumin, dried thyme, dried oregano, ground black pepper, and salt to taste.
8. Stir well to combine.

Simmer the Soup:
9. Bring the soup to a boil, then reduce the heat to low and let it simmer for 15-20 minutes, or until the vegetables are tender.

Add the Remaining Ingredients:
10. Add the broccoli florets, purple cabbage, and chopped kale to the pot.
11. Cook for another 5-7 minutes, until the broccoli is tender and the kale is wilted.

Finish the Soup:
12. Stir in the chopped fresh parsley and basil (if using).
13. Add lemon juice if desired for a bright, fresh flavor.
14. Adjust the seasoning with additional salt and pepper if needed.

NOT YOUR ORDINARY CHICKEN, VEGETABLE & WILD RICE SOUP

Time: 70 minutes
Serving size: 2

The magic is in the spices. If you substitute the chicken for tofu, make sure to use a firm variety.

Nutritional Information (Approximate per 1 serving):
Calories: 250 kcal | Protein: 18g | Carbohydrates: 30g | Dietary Fiber: 5g | Sugars: 5g | Fat: 8g | Saturated Fat: 1g | Sodium: 400mg

Beneficial Nutrients & Anti-Inflammatories:
Onion: Quercetin, antioxidants | Garlic: Allicin, antioxidants | Carrots: Beta-carotene, vitamin A | Celery: Apigenin, antioxidants | Red Bell Pepper: Vitamin C, antioxidants | Butternut Squash: Beta-carotene, vitamins A and C | Spinach: Vitamins A, C, K, antioxidants | Wild Rice: Fiber, magnesium, antioxidants | Chicken: Lean protein | Olive Oil: Monounsaturated fats, antioxidants | Turmeric: Curcumin | Ginger: Gingerol, other antioxidants | Lemon: Vitamin C, antioxidants | Parsley: Vitamin C, flavonoids

Ingredients:

For the Soup:

- 2 tablespoons olive oil (27.2g; 0.96oz)
- 1 large onion, diced (~200g)
- 3 cloves garlic, minced (~9g)
- 3 carrots, sliced (180g)
- 3 celery stalks, sliced (~120g)
- 1 red bell pepper, diced (~120g)
- 1 cup butternut squash, peeled and diced (136g)
- 1 teaspoon ground turmeric (3g)
- 1 teaspoon ground cumin (3g)
- 1/2 teaspoon ground black pepper (1.2g)
- 1 teaspoon dried thyme (1g)
- 1 teaspoon dried rosemary (1g)

- 6 cups chicken broth (preferably low sodium) (1440g; 50.7oz)
- 1 cup wild rice, rinsed (185g)
- 2 cups cooked chicken breast, shredded or diced (280g)
- 2 cups baby spinach, chopped (60g)
- 1 tablespoon fresh ginger, grated (6g)
- 2 tablespoons fresh lemon juice (30g; 1.02oz)
- 1/2 teaspoon maple syrup (optional) (3.5g)
- 1/4 cup fresh parsley, chopped (4g)
- Salt to taste (~1.5g)

Directions:

Prepare the Soup Base:

1. In a large pot, heat the olive oil over medium heat.
2. Add the diced onion and sauté until translucent, about 5 minutes.
3. Add the minced garlic and cook for another minute until fragrant.

Add the Vegetables and Spices:

4. Add the sliced carrots, celery, red bell pepper, and butternut squash to the pot.
5. Stir in the ground turmeric, ground cumin, ground black pepper, dried thyme, and dried rosemary.
6. Cook for about 5-7 minutes, stirring occasionally.

Add the Broth and Rice:

7. Pour in the chicken broth and add the rinsed wild rice.
8. Bring the mixture to a boil, then reduce the heat to low and let it simmer for 45-50 minutes, or until the rice is tender.

Add the Chicken and Spinach:

9. Stir in the cooked chicken and chopped spinach.
10. Cook for another 5-7 minutes, or until the spinach is wilted and the chicken is heated through.

Finish the Soup:

11. Stir in the grated fresh ginger, fresh lemon juice, and maple syrup (if using).
12. Taste and adjust the seasoning with additional salt and pepper if needed.
13. Stir in the chopped fresh parsley.

COCONUT-CURRY STEW WITH SWEET POTATO & RICE

Time: 45 minutes
Serving size: 4

I think about this stew in my sleep. Curry, sweet potato, light fish? Yep. It's that good. And loaded with the good stuff.

Nutritional Information (Approximate per 1 serving):

Calories: 450 kcal | Protein: 30g | Carbohydrates: 50g | Dietary Fiber: 8g |
Sugars: 10g | Fat: 18g | Saturated Fat: 12g | Sodium: 600mg

Beneficial Nutrients & Anti-Inflammatories:

Onion: Quercetin, antioxidants | Garlic: Allicin, antioxidants | Ginger: Gingerol, other antioxidants | Red Bell Pepper: Vitamin C, antioxidants | Yellow Bell Pepper: Vitamin C, antioxidants | Sweet Potatoes: Beta-carotene, vitamins A and C | Coconut Milk: Lauric acid, antioxidants | Cod: Lean protein, omega-3 fatty acids | Turmeric: Curcumin | Cumin: Cuminaldehyde, other antioxidants | Coriander: Antioxidants, vitamin C | Spinach: Vitamins A, C, K, antioxidants | Cilantro: Vitamin C, flavonoids | Lime: Vitamin C, antioxidants

Ingredients:

For the Stew:

- 2 tablespoons coconut oil or olive oil (27.2g; 0.96oz)
- 1 large onion, diced (~200g)
- 3 cloves garlic, minced (~9g)
- 1 tablespoon fresh ginger, grated (6g)
- 1 red bell pepper, diced (~120g)
- 1 yellow bell pepper, diced (~120g)
- 2 medium sweet potatoes, peeled and diced (~400g)
- 1 can (14 ounces) diced tomatoes (400g)
- 1 can (14 ounces) full-fat coconut milk (400g)
- 4 cups vegetable or fish broth (960g; 33.8oz)
- 2 tablespoons red curry paste (30g)

- 1 teaspoon ground turmeric (3g)
- 1 teaspoon ground cumin (3g)
- 1/2 teaspoon ground coriander (1g)
- Salt and pepper to taste (~1.5g salt; ~0.6g pepper)
- (Optional) 1 pound cod fillets, cut into chunks (or a protein of your choice) (454g)
- 1 cup baby spinach, chopped (30g)
- 1/4 cup fresh cilantro, chopped (4g)
- 2 tablespoons fresh lime juice (30g; 1.02oz)

For the Rice:

- 1 cup jasmine or basmati rice (185g)
- 2 cups water or vegetable broth (480g; 16.9oz)
- Pinch of salt (~0.5g)

Directions:

Prepare the Rice:

1. In a medium saucepan, bring the water or vegetable broth to a boil. Add the rice and a pinch of salt.
2. Reduce the heat to low, cover, and simmer for 15 minutes, or until the rice is cooked and the liquid is absorbed.
3. Remove from heat and let it sit, covered, for 5 minutes. Fluff with a fork and set aside.

Prepare the Stew:

4. In a large pot, heat the coconut oil over medium heat.
5. Add the diced onion and sauté until translucent, about 5 minutes.
6. Add the minced garlic and grated ginger, and cook for another minute until fragrant.
7. Add the diced red and yellow bell peppers and cook for another 3-4 minutes.
8. Stir in the diced sweet potatoes, diced tomatoes, coconut milk, and vegetable or fish broth.
9. Add the red curry paste, ground turmeric, ground cumin, and ground coriander. Stir well to combine.
10. Bring the stew to a boil, then reduce the heat to low and let it simmer for 20-25 minutes, or until the sweet potatoes are tender.

Add the Protein (optional) and Spinach:

11. Gently stir in the cod chunks and chopped spinach.
12. Cook for another 5-7 minutes, or until the cod is cooked through and the spinach is wilted. Depending on your protein, your cook time here may vary.

Finish the Stew:

13. Stir in the fresh cilantro and lime juice.
14. Taste and adjust the seasoning with additional salt and pepper if needed.

AVGOLEMONO (LEMON GREEK SOUP)

Time: 40 minutes
Serving size: 6

This one takes a little practice as you add the tempered lemon and egg mixture into the soup, but once you get it...you'll GET it. It's absolutely nóstimo.

Nutritional Information (Approximate per 1 serving):

Calories: 300 kcal | Protein: 25g | Carbohydrates: 25g | Dietary Fiber: 3g | Sugars: 4g
| Fat: 10g | Saturated Fat: 2g | Sodium: 600mg

Beneficial Nutrients & Anti-Inflammatories:

Onion: Quercetin, antioxidants | Garlic: Allicin, antioxidants | Carrots: Beta-carotene, vitamin A | Celery: Apigenin, antioxidants | Chicken: Lean protein | Olive Oil: Monounsaturated fats, antioxidants | Spinach: Vitamins A, C, K, antioxidants | Lemon: Vitamin C, antioxidants | Dill: Flavonoids, antioxidants | Parsley: Vitamin C, flavonoids

Ingredients:

For the Soup:

- 2 tablespoons olive oil (27.2g; 0.96oz)
- 1 large onion, diced (~200g)
- 2 cloves garlic, minced (~6g)
- 3 carrots, sliced (180g)
- 2 celery stalks, sliced (~80g)
- 8 cups chicken or vegetable broth (preferably low sodium) (1920g; 67.6oz)
- 1 cup orzo or rice (170g for orzo; 185g for rice)

- 2 cups cooked chicken breast, shredded or diced (or a protein of your choice) (280g)
- 3 large eggs (150g)
- 1/3 cup fresh lemon juice (80g; 2.7oz)
- 1 teaspoon dried oregano (1g)
- Salt and pepper to taste (~1.5g salt; ~0.6g pepper)
- 2 cups baby spinach, chopped (60g)
- 1/4 cup fresh dill, chopped (4g)
- 1/4 cup fresh parsley, chopped (4g)

Directions:

Prepare the Soup Base:

1. In a large pot, heat the olive oil over medium heat.
2. Add the diced onion and sauté until translucent, about 5 minutes.
3. Add the minced garlic and cook for another minute until fragrant.
4. Add the sliced carrots and celery, and cook for another 3-4 minutes, stirring occasionally.

Add the Broth and Orzo/Rice:

5. Pour in the broth and bring the mixture to a boil.
6. Add the orzo or rice and reduce the heat to a simmer. Cook for about 10-12 minutes, or until the orzo or rice is tender.

Add the Chicken:

7. Stir in the shredded or diced chicken and cook until heated through, about 5 minutes.

Prepare the Avgolemono (Egg-Lemon Mixture):

8. In a medium bowl, whisk the eggs until frothy.
9. Gradually whisk in the lemon juice until well combined.
10. Slowly ladle 1-2 cups of the hot soup broth into the egg-lemon mixture, whisking constantly to temper the eggs.

Finish the Soup:

11. Gradually pour the tempered egg-lemon mixture back into the soup, stirring constantly.
12. Cook for another 2-3 minutes, but do not let the soup boil.
13. Stir in the dried oregano, chopped spinach, fresh dill, and fresh parsley.
14. Season with salt and pepper to taste.

CURRIED CAULIFLOWER SOUP

Time: 55 minutes
Serving size: 4

Spicy, fragrant, and packed with goodness. This one will make your house smell amazing too.

Nutritional Information (Approximate per 1 serving):

Calories: 250 kcal | Protein: 5g | Carbohydrates: 18g | Dietary Fiber: 6g | Sugars: 6g | Fat: 18g | Saturated Fat: 14g | Sodium: 450mg

Beneficial Nutrients & Anti-Inflammatories:

Onion: Quercetin, antioxidants | Garlic: Allicin, antioxidants | Ginger: Gingerol, other antioxidants | Cauliflower: Glucosinolates, vitamin C, antioxidants | Coconut Milk: Lauric acid, antioxidants | Turmeric: Curcumin | Cumin: Cuminaldehyde, other antioxidants | Coriander: Antioxidants, vitamin C | Cilantro: Vitamin C, flavonoids | Lime: Vitamin C, antioxidants

Ingredients:

For the Soup:

- 2 tablespoons coconut oil or olive oil (27.2g; 0.96oz)
- 1 large onion, diced (~200g)
- 3 cloves garlic, minced (~9g)
- 1 tablespoon fresh ginger, grated (6g)
- 1 tablespoon curry powder (6g)
- 1 teaspoon ground turmeric (3g)
- 1 large head cauliflower, chopped (~840g)
- 1 can (14 ounces) coconut milk (400g)
- 4 cups vegetable broth (960g; 33.8oz)
- 1 teaspoon ground cumin (3g)
- 1 teaspoon ground coriander (1g)
- Salt and pepper to taste (~1.5g salt; ~0.6g pepper)
- 1/4 cup fresh cilantro, chopped (4g)
- 1 tablespoon fresh lime juice (optional) (15g; 0.5oz)

Directions:

Prepare the Soup Base:

1. In a large pot, heat the coconut oil over medium heat.
2. Add the diced onion and sauté until translucent, about 5 minutes.
3. Add the minced garlic and grated ginger, and cook for another minute until fragrant.

Add the Spices and Cauliflower:

4. Stir in the curry powder, ground turmeric, ground cumin, and ground coriander.
5. Add the chopped cauliflower and cook for another 5 minutes, stirring occasionally.

Add the Broth and Coconut Milk:

6. Pour in the vegetable broth and coconut milk, and bring the mixture to a boil.
7. Reduce the heat to low and let it simmer for 20-25 minutes, or until the cauliflower is tender.

Blend the Soup:

8. Using an immersion blender, blend the soup until smooth.
9. Alternatively, you can transfer the soup in batches to a blender and blend until smooth.

Finish the Soup:

10. Stir in the fresh cilantro and lime juice (if using).
11. Taste and adjust the seasoning with additional salt and pepper if needed.

SPICED CARROT & GINGER SOUP

Time: 50 minutes
Serving size: 4

Turmeric, cumin, coriander, cinnamon, black pepper, and ginger. It's spicy (but not hot spicy) and really, really good for you.

Nutritional Information (Approximate per 1 serving):
Calories: 200 kcal | Protein: 3g | Carbohydrates: 30g | Dietary Fiber: 8g |
Sugars: 15g | Fat: 8g | Saturated Fat: 1g | Sodium: 400mg

Beneficial Nutrients & Anti-Inflammatories:

Onion: Quercetin, antioxidants | Garlic: Allicin, antioxidants | Ginger: Gingerol, other antioxidants | Carrots: Beta-carotene, vitamin A | Olive Oil: Monounsaturated fats, antioxidants | Turmeric: Curcumin | Cumin: Cuminaldehyde, other antioxidants | Coriander: Antioxidants, vitamin C | Parsley: Vitamin C, flavonoids | Lemon: Vitamin C, antioxidants

Ingredients:

For the Soup:

- 2 tablespoons olive oil (27.2g; 0.96oz)
- 1 large onion, diced (~200g)
- 3 cloves garlic, minced (~9g)
- 1 tablespoon fresh ginger, grated (6g)
- 6 large carrots, peeled and sliced (~450g)
- 4 cups vegetable broth (960g; 33.8oz)
- 1 teaspoon ground turmeric (3g)
- 1 teaspoon ground cumin (3g)
- 1/2 teaspoon ground coriander (1g)

- 1/4 teaspoon ground cinnamon (0.65g)
- 1/4 teaspoon ground black pepper (0.6g)
- Salt to taste (~1.5g)
- 1/4 cup fresh parsley, chopped (4g)
- 1 tablespoon fresh lemon juice (15g; 0.5oz)

Directions:

Prepare the Soup Base:

1. In a large pot, heat the olive oil over medium heat.
2. Add the diced onion and sauté until translucent, about 5 minutes.
3. Add the minced garlic and grated ginger, and cook for another minute until fragrant.

Add the Carrots and Spices:

4. Stir in the sliced carrots, ground turmeric, ground cumin, ground coriander, ground cinnamon, and ground black pepper.
5. Cook for another 5 minutes, stirring occasionally.

Add the Broth:

6. Pour in the vegetable broth and bring the mixture to a boil.
7. Reduce the heat to low and let it simmer for 20-25 minutes, or until the carrots are tender.

Blend the Soup:

8. Using an immersion blender, blend the soup until smooth.
9. Alternatively, you can transfer the soup in batches to a blender and blend until smooth.

Finish the Soup:

10. Stir in the fresh parsley and lemon juice.
11. Taste and adjust the seasoning with additional salt if needed.

SWEET POTATO & RED LENTIL SOUP

Time: 50 minutes
Serving size: 4

A vegan powerhouse loaded with fiber, vitamins, antioxidants, and healthy fats.

Nutritional Information (Approximate per 1 serving):
Calories: 300 kcal | Protein: 12g | Carbohydrates: 45g | Dietary Fiber:
12g | Sugars: 8g | Fat: 8g | Saturated Fat: 1g | Sodium: 500mg

Beneficial Nutrients & Anti-Inflammatories:

Onion: Quercetin, antioxidants | Garlic: Allicin, antioxidants | Ginger: Gingerol, other antioxidants | Sweet Potatoes: Beta-carotene, vitamins A and C | Red Lentils: Fiber, protein, antioxidants | Olive Oil: Monounsaturated fats, antioxidants | Turmeric: Curcumin | Cumin: Cuminaldehyde, other antioxidants | Coriander: Antioxidants, vitamin C | Cilantro: Vitamin C, flavonoids | Lemon: Vitamin C, antioxidants

Ingredients:

For the Soup:

- 2 tablespoons olive oil (27.2g; 0.96oz)
- 1 large onion, diced (~200g)
- 3 cloves garlic, minced (~9g)
- 1 tablespoon fresh ginger, grated (6g)
- 2 medium sweet potatoes, peeled and diced (~400g)
- 1 cup red lentils, rinsed (200g)
- 6 cups vegetable broth (1440g; 50.7oz)
- 1 teaspoon ground turmeric (3g)
- 1 teaspoon ground cumin (3g)
- 1 teaspoon ground coriander (1g)
- 1/2 teaspoon ground cinnamon (1.3g)
- Salt and pepper to taste (~1.5g salt; ~0.6g pepper)
- 1/4 cup fresh cilantro, chopped (4g)
- 1 tablespoon fresh lemon juice (15g; 0.5oz)

Directions:

Prepare the Soup Base:

1. In a large pot, heat the olive oil over medium heat.
2. Add the diced onion and sauté until translucent, about 5 minutes.
3. Add the minced garlic and grated ginger, and cook for another minute until fragrant.

Add the Sweet Potatoes and Spices:

4. Stir in the diced sweet potatoes, ground turmeric, ground cumin, ground coriander, and ground cinnamon.
5. Cook for another 5 minutes, stirring occasionally.
6. Add the Lentils and Broth:
7. Add the rinsed red lentils and vegetable broth.
8. Bring the mixture to a boil, then reduce the heat to low and let it simmer for 20-25 minutes, or until the lentils and sweet potatoes are tender.

Blend the Soup (Optional):

9. For a smoother soup, you can use an immersion blender to partially blend the soup, leaving some chunks for texture.
10. Alternatively, you can blend half of the soup in a blender and then return it to the pot.

Finish the Soup:

11. Stir in the fresh cilantro and lemon juice.
12. Taste and adjust the seasoning with additional salt and pepper if needed.

TANTALIZING TURMERIC LENTIL & SPINACH SOUP

Time: 50 minutes
Serving size: 4

You'll find turmeric throughout this book because it's an anti-inflammatory wonder spice. The combination here works really nicely and tastes amazing.

Nutritional Information (Approximate per 1 serving):
Calories: 250 kcal | Protein: 12g | Carbohydrates: 38g | Dietary Fiber: 10g | Sugars: 7g | Fat: 8g | Saturated Fat: 1g | Sodium: 500mg

Beneficial Nutrients & Anti-Inflammatories:

Onion: Quercetin, antioxidants | Garlic: Allicin, antioxidants | Ginger: Gingerol, other antioxidants | Carrots: Beta-carotene, vitamin A | Celery: Apigenin, antioxidants | Lentils: Fiber, protein, antioxidants | Spinach: Vitamins A, C, K, antioxidants | Olive Oil: Monounsaturated fats, antioxidants | Turmeric: Curcumin | Cumin: Cuminaldehyde, other antioxidants | Coriander: Antioxidants, vitamin C | Cilantro: Vitamin C, flavonoids | Lemon: Vitamin C, antioxidants

Ingredients:

For the Soup:

- 2 tablespoons olive oil (27.2g; 0.96oz)
- 1 large onion, diced (~200g)
- 3 cloves garlic, minced (~9g)
- 1 tablespoon fresh ginger, grated (6g)
- 2 carrots, sliced (~120g)
- 2 celery stalks, sliced (~80g)
- 1 cup dried green or brown lentils, rinsed (200g)
- 6 cups vegetable broth (1440g; 50.7oz)
- 1 1/2 teaspoons ground turmeric (4.5g)

- 1 teaspoon ground cumin (3g)
- 1 teaspoon ground coriander (1g)
- 1/4 teaspoon ground black pepper (0.6g)
- Salt to taste (~1.5g)
- 2 cups baby spinach, chopped (60g)
- 1/4 cup fresh cilantro, chopped (4g)
- 1 tablespoon fresh lemon juice (15g; 0.5oz)

Directions:

Prepare the Soup Base:

1. In a large pot, heat the olive oil over medium heat.
2. Add the diced onion and sauté until translucent, about 5 minutes.
3. Add the minced garlic and grated ginger, and cook for another minute until fragrant.

Add the Vegetables and Lentils:

4. Stir in the sliced carrots and celery, and cook for another 5 minutes.
5. Add the rinsed lentils, vegetable broth, ground turmeric, ground cumin, ground coriander, ground black pepper, and salt to taste.
6. Bring the mixture to a boil, then reduce the heat to low and let it simmer for 30-35 minutes, or until the lentils and vegetables are tender.

Add the Spinach:

7. Stir in the chopped baby spinach and cook for another 5 minutes, or until the spinach is wilted.

Finish the Soup:

8. Stir in the chopped fresh cilantro and lemon juice.
9. Taste and adjust the seasoning with additional salt and pepper if needed.

TOMATO BASIL SOUP

Time: 50 minutes
Serving size: 4

Who doesn't love tomato soup? The key here is to use low or no-sodium canned tomatoes. Or, you can use fresh...up to you. I like canned, but that's just my personal preference.

Nutritional Information (Approximate per 1 serving):

Calories: 180 kcal | Protein: 4g | Carbohydrates: 24g | Dietary Fiber: 8g | Sugars: 5g | Fat: 8g | Saturated Fat: 1g | Sodium: 250-500mg

Beneficial Nutrients & Anti-Inflammatories:

Onion: Quercetin, antioxidants | Garlic: Allicin, antioxidants | Tomatoes: Lycopene, vitamin C | Olive Oil: Monounsaturated fats, antioxidants | Basil: Eucalyptol, antioxidants | Oregano: Carvacrol, antioxidants | Thyme: Thymol, antioxidants | Parsley: Vitamin C, flavonoids | Balsamic Vinegar: Polyphenols, antioxidants

Ingredients:

For the Soup:

- 2 tablespoons olive oil (27.2g; 0.96oz)
- 1 large onion, diced (~200g)
- 4 cloves garlic, minced (~12g)
- 2 cans (28 ounces each) low or no-sodium diced tomatoes (1590g total)
- 4 cups vegetable broth (960g; 33.8oz)
- 1 teaspoon dried oregano (1g)
- 1 teaspoon dried thyme (1g)

- 1/2 teaspoon ground black pepper (1.2g)
- Salt to taste (~1.5g)
- 1/4 cup fresh basil leaves, chopped (5g)
- 1/4 cup fresh parsley, chopped (4g)
- 1 tablespoon balsamic vinegar (15g; 0.5oz)

Directions:

Prepare the Soup Base:

1. In a large pot, heat the olive oil over medium heat.
2. Add the diced onion and sauté until translucent, about 5 minutes.
3. Add the minced garlic and cook for another minute until fragrant.

Add the Tomatoes and Spices:

4. Stir in the diced tomatoes, vegetable broth, dried oregano, dried thyme, ground black pepper, and salt to taste.
5. Bring the mixture to a boil, then reduce the heat to low and let it simmer for 20-25 minutes.

Blend the Soup:

6. Using an immersion blender, blend the soup until smooth.
7. Alternatively, you can transfer the soup in batches to a blender and blend until smooth.

Finish the Soup:

8. Stir in the chopped fresh basil, fresh parsley, and balsamic vinegar.
9. Taste and adjust the seasoning with additional salt if needed.

CHAPTER 6:
LUNCH & DINNER ENTRÉES

BAKED SWEET POTATOES WITH TAHINI SAUCE

Time: 35 minutes
Serving size: 4

It doesn't get any easier than this. You bake a sweet potato and add a delicious sauce to it. Healthy, anti-inflammatory, and delish.

Nutritional Information (Approximate per 1 serving):

Calories: 250 kcal | Protein: 4g | Carbohydrates: 40g | Dietary Fiber: 7g | Sugars: 10g | Fat: 10g | Saturated Fat: 1.5g | Sodium: 250mg

Beneficial Nutrients & Anti-Inflammatories:

Sweet Potatoes: Beta-carotene, vitamins A and C | Tahini: Healthy fats, antioxidants | Garlic: Allicin, antioxidants | Lemon: Vitamin C, antioxidants | Olive Oil: Monounsaturated fats, antioxidants | Pomegranate Seeds: Punicalagins, vitamin C, antioxidants | Parsley: Vitamin C, flavonoids

Ingredients:

For the Sweet Potatoes:

- 4 medium sweet potatoes, scrubbed and halved lengthwise (~800g total)
- 2 tablespoons olive oil (27.2g; 0.96oz)
- 1 tablespoon chili powder (7.5g)
- Salt and pepper to taste (~1.5g salt; ~0.6g pepper)

For the Tahini Sauce:

- 1/4 cup tahini (60g)
- 2 tablespoons lemon juice (30g; 1.02oz)
- 2 tablespoons water (or as needed for consistency) (30g; 1.02oz)

- 1 clove garlic, minced (~3g)
- 1/4 teaspoon ground cumin (1.1g)
- 1/4 teaspoon ground paprika (0.5g)
- Salt to taste (~1.5g)

For the Toppings:

- 1/4 cup fresh parsley, chopped (4g)
- 1/4 cup pomegranate seeds (40g)

Directions:

Prepare the Sweet Potatoes:

1. Preheat your oven to 400°F (200°C).
2. Place the sweet potatoes on a baking sheet, flesh side up.
3. Drizzle with olive oil and season with chili powder, salt and pepper.
4. Bake for 25-30 minutes, until tender and slightly caramelized.

Prepare the Tahini Sauce:

5. In a small bowl, whisk together the tahini, lemon juice, water, minced garlic, ground cumin, ground paprika, and salt. Adjust the water quantity to achieve your desired consistency.

BEET THAT FALAFEL SLIDERS

Time: 25 minutes
Serving size: 2

That's beeT, not beeF. Beets are jam packed full of betalains, fiber, and vitamin C. Add some dairy-free tzatziki to these and thank me later.

Nutritional Information (Approximate per 1 serving):

Calories: 350 kcal | Protein: 10g | Carbohydrates: 45g | Dietary Fiber: 8g |
Sugars: 6g | Fat: 14g | Saturated Fat: 2g | Sodium: 400mg

Beneficial Nutrients & Anti-Inflammatories:

Beets: Betalains, fiber, vitamin C | Chickpeas: Fiber, protein, antioxidants | Garlic: Allicin, antioxidants | Turmeric: Curcumin | Olive Oil: Monounsaturated fats, antioxidants | Parsley: Vitamin C, flavonoids | Spinach: Vitamins A, C, K, antioxidants | Red Onion: Quercetin, antioxidants

ANTI-INFLAMMATORY DIET & COOKBOOK

....

Ingredients:

For the Beet Falafel:

- 1 cup cooked red beets, grated (typically one large red beet, or two medium-sized red beets) (~150g)
- 1 can (15 ounces) chickpeas, drained and rinsed (425g)
- 1/2 cup fresh parsley, chopped (8g)
- 2 cloves garlic, minced (~6g)
- 1 teaspoon ground cumin (3g)
- 1 teaspoon ground coriander (1g)
- 1/2 teaspoon ground turmeric (1.5g)
- 1/2 teaspoon ground black pepper (1.2g)

- Salt to taste (~1.5g)
- 1/4 cup chickpea flour (or all-purpose flour) (30g for chickpea flour; 31g for all-purpose flour)
- 2 tablespoons olive oil (27.2g; 0.96oz)

For the Sliders:

- 8 slider buns or small whole wheat buns (~320g total)
- 1 cup baby spinach leaves (30g)
- 1/2 red onion, thinly sliced (~60g)
- 1/2 cup dairy-free tzatziki sauce (store-bought or homemade) (~120g)

....

Directions:

Prepare the Beet Falafel Mixture:

1. In a food processor, combine the grated beets, chickpeas, fresh parsley, minced garlic, ground cumin, ground coriander, ground turmeric, ground black pepper, and salt. Pulse until the mixture is well combined but still slightly chunky.
2. Transfer the mixture to a bowl and stir in the chickpea flour. Form the mixture into small patties.

Cook the Falafel Patties:

3. In a large skillet, heat the olive oil over medium heat.
4. Add the falafel patties and cook for about 3-4 minutes per side, until golden brown and crispy.

Assemble the Sliders:

5. Toast the slider buns if desired.
6. Spread a layer of dairy-free tzatziki sauce on the bottom half of each bun.
7. Top with baby spinach leaves, a beet falafel patty, and thinly sliced red onion.
8. Place the top half of the bun on the slider.

COLLARD GREEN VEGETARIAN WRAPS

Time: 45 minutes
Serving size: 2

Collard greens are loaded with anti-inflammatory goodness, and make for a great wrap where you can pack in even more anti-inflammatories. This recipe uses black beans, but you could use any bean of your choice.

Nutritional Information (Approximate per 1 serving):

Calories: 300 kcal | Protein: 10g | Carbohydrates: 40g | Dietary Fiber: 10g | Sugars: 4g | Fat: 12g | Saturated Fat: 1.5g | Sodium: 250mg

Beneficial Nutrients & Anti-Inflammatories:

Collard Greens: Vitamins A, C, K, antioxidants | Quinoa: Fiber, magnesium, antioxidants | Black Beans: Fiber, protein, antioxidants | Garlic: Allicin, antioxidants | Tahini: Healthy fats, antioxidants | Lemon: Vitamin C, antioxidants | Avocado: Monounsaturated fats, vitamin E, antioxidants | Cilantro: Vitamin C, flavonoids | Parsley: Vitamin C, flavonoids | Bell Peppers: Vitamin C, antioxidants

Ingredients:

For the Wraps:

- 8 large collard green leaves, stems removed (~200g total)
- 1 cup cooked quinoa (185g)
- 1 can (15 ounces) black beans, drained and rinsed (425g)
- 1 red bell pepper, thinly sliced (~120g)
- 1 avocado, sliced (~200g)
- 1/2 cup shredded carrots (55g)
- 1/4 cup fresh cilantro, chopped (4g)
- 1/4 cup fresh parsley, chopped (4g)

For the Tahini-Lemon Sauce:

- 1/4 cup tahini (60g)
- 2 tablespoons lemon juice (30g; 1.02oz)
- 2 tablespoons water (or as needed for consistency) (30g; 1.02oz)
- 1 clove garlic, minced (~3g)
- 1/4 teaspoon ground cumin (1.1g)
- Salt to taste (~1.5g)

Directions:

Prepare the Tahini-Lemon Sauce:

1. In a small bowl, whisk together the tahini, lemon juice, water, minced garlic, ground cumin, and salt. Adjust the water quantity to achieve your desired consistency.

Prepare the Collard Green Leaves:

2. Bring a large pot of water to a boil. Blanch the collard green leaves for about 30 seconds, then transfer them to a bowl of ice water to stop the cooking process. Pat the leaves dry with paper towels.

Assemble the Wraps:

3. Lay a collard green leaf flat on a surface.
4. Spread a tablespoon of the tahini-lemon sauce over the leaf.
5. Add a portion of the cooked quinoa, black beans, sliced red bell pepper, avocado, shredded carrots, fresh cilantro, and fresh parsley.
6. Roll the collard green leaf like a burrito, folding in the sides as you roll.
7. Repeat with the remaining leaves and filling.

GREEN SHAKSHUKA

Time: 30 minutes
Serving size: 4

A green twist on the classic shakshuka, loaded with spinach, kale, parsley, cilantro, and all of the anti-inflammatory spices your heart desires.

Nutritional Information (Approximate per 1 serving):

Calories: 300 kcal | Protein: 15g | Carbohydrates: 12g | Dietary Fiber: 4g | Sugars: 4g | Fat: 22g | Saturated Fat: 5g | Sodium: 350mg

Beneficial Nutrients & Anti-Inflammatories:

Onion: Quercetin, antioxidants | Garlic: Allicin, antioxidants | Spinach: Vitamins A, C, K, antioxidants | Kale: Vitamins A, C, K, antioxidants | Zucchini: Vitamin C, manganese, antioxidants | Cilantro: Vitamin C, flavonoids | Parsley: Vitamin C, flavonoids | Olive Oil: Monounsaturated fats, antioxidants | Turmeric: Curcumin | Cumin: Cuminaldehyde, other antioxidants | Coriander: Antioxidants, vitamin C

Ingredients:

For the Shakshuka:

- 2 tablespoons olive oil (27.2g; 0.96oz)
- 1 large onion, diced (~200g)
- 3 cloves garlic, minced (~9g)
- 1 large green bell pepper, diced (~120g)
- 2 cups fresh spinach, chopped (60g)
- 2 cups kale, chopped (60g)
- 1 zucchini, diced (~200g)
- 1 cup fresh cilantro, chopped (16g)
- 1 cup fresh parsley, chopped (16g)
- 1 teaspoon ground cumin (3g)
- 1 teaspoon ground coriander (1g)
- 1/2 teaspoon ground turmeric (1.5g)
- 1/2 teaspoon ground black pepper (1.2g)
- Salt to taste (~1.5g)
- 1/2 cup vegetable broth or water (120g; 4.2oz)

- 6 large eggs (300g total)

For the Garnish:

- 1/4 cup crumbled feta cheese (optional, use dairy-free cheese for a non-dairy option) (35g)
- 1/4 cup fresh cilantro, chopped (4g)
- 1/4 cup fresh parsley, chopped (4g)
- 1 avocado, sliced (optional) (~200g)
- 1 tablespoon lemon juice (15g; 0.5oz)

Directions:

Prepare the Base:
1. In a large skillet, heat the olive oil over medium heat.
2. Add the diced onion and sauté until translucent, about 5 minutes.
3. Add the minced garlic and cook for another minute until fragrant.

Add the Vegetables:
4. Add the diced green bell pepper, chopped spinach, chopped kale, and diced zucchini to the skillet.
5. Cook for about 5-7 minutes until the vegetables are tender.

Add the Spices:
6. Stir in the chopped cilantro, chopped parsley, ground cumin, ground coriander, ground turmeric, ground black pepper, and salt.
7. Pour in the vegetable broth or water and stir to combine.

Create the Sauce:
8. Reduce the heat to low and let the mixture simmer for about 5 minutes until the greens are wilted and the flavors have melded together.

Add the Eggs:
9. Make 6 small wells in the vegetable mixture.
10. Crack an egg into each well.
11. Cover the skillet and cook for about 5-7 minutes, or until the eggs are cooked to your desired doneness.

Garnish and Serve:
12. Sprinkle the shakshuka with crumbled feta cheese (if using), fresh cilantro, fresh parsley, and sliced avocado (if using).
13. Drizzle with lemon juice before serving.

GRILLED CHICKEN WITH RED PEPPER-PECAN ROMESCO SAUCE

Time: 35 minutes
Serving size: 4

If you haven't had romesco sauce before, you don't know what you're missing. It's peppery, slightly smoky, and addictive. Delish.

Nutritional Information (Approximate per 1 serving):

Calories: 450 kcal | Protein: 35g | Carbohydrates: 10g | Dietary Fiber: 3g |
Sugars: 4g | Fat: 30g | Saturated Fat: 4.5g | Sodium: 300mg

Beneficial Nutrients & Anti-Inflammatories:

Chicken: Lean protein | Red Bell Peppers: Vitamin C, antioxidants | Pecans: Healthy fats, antioxidants | Garlic: Allicin, antioxidants | Olive Oil: Monounsaturated fats, antioxidants | Paprika: Capsaicin, antioxidants | Cumin: Cuminaldehyde, other antioxidants | Parsley: Vitamin C, flavonoids

Ingredients:

For the Grilled Chicken:

- 4 boneless, skinless chicken breasts (~680g total)
- 2 tablespoons olive oil (27.2g; 0.96oz)
- 1 teaspoon garlic powder (3.3g)
- 1 teaspoon paprika (2.3g)
- 1/2 teaspoon ground black pepper (1.2g)
- Salt to taste (~1.5g)
- 1 tablespoon lemon juice (15g; 0.5oz)

For the Red Pepper-Pecan Romesco Sauce:

- 2 large red bell peppers (~240g total)
- 1/2 cup pecans, toasted (60g)
- 2 cloves garlic, minced (~6g)

- 1/4 cup olive oil (54.4g; 1.92oz)
- 2 tablespoons red wine vinegar (30g; 1.02oz)
- 1 teaspoon smoked paprika (2.3g)
- 1/2 teaspoon ground cumin (1.5g)
- 1/4 teaspoon cayenne pepper (optional) (0.5g)
- Salt and pepper to taste (~1.5g salt; ~0.6g pepper)
- 1/4 cup fresh parsley, chopped (for garnish) (4g)

Directions:

Prepare the Chicken:

1. Preheat your grill to medium-high heat.
2. In a small bowl, mix together the olive oil, garlic powder, paprika, ground black pepper, salt, and lemon juice.
3. Rub the mixture over the chicken breasts, coating them evenly.
4. Grill the chicken for about 6-8 minutes per side, or until the internal temperature reaches 165°F (75°C) and the chicken is cooked through. Remove from the grill and let it rest.

Prepare the Red Pepper-Pecan Romesco Sauce:

5. While the chicken is grilling, roast the red bell peppers over the grill or directly over a gas burner until the skins are charred and blackened on all sides. Alternatively, you can roast them in the oven at 450°F (230°C) for about 20 minutes.
6. Place the roasted peppers in a bowl and cover with a plate or plastic wrap. Let them steam for about 10 minutes, then peel off the skins, remove the seeds, and chop the peppers.
7. In a food processor, combine the roasted red bell peppers, toasted pecans, minced garlic, olive oil, red wine vinegar, smoked paprika, ground cumin, cayenne pepper (if using), salt, and pepper. Blend until smooth and well combined.

Serve:

8. Slice the grilled chicken breasts and place them on serving plates.
9. Spoon the Red Pepper-Pecan Romesco Sauce over the chicken.
10. Garnish with fresh parsley.

GRILLED HONEY-CHIPOTLE SALMON FOIL PACKETS WITH SUMMER SQUASH

Time: 45 minutes
Serving size: 4

Good for the summertime. The foil packets make cooking a breeze, and cleanup easy as can be. This recipe has a lot of beneficial nutrients as well.

Nutritional Information (Approximate per 1 serving):

Calories: 450 kcal | Protein: 30g | Carbohydrates: 30g | Dietary Fiber: 4g | Sugars: 20g | Fat: 25g | Saturated Fat: 4g | Sodium: 400mg

Beneficial Nutrients & Anti-Inflammatories:

Salmon: Omega-3 fatty acids (EPA and DHA) | Honey: Antioxidants | Chipotle Chili Powder: Capsaicin, antioxidants | Garlic: Allicin, antioxidants | Olive Oil: Monounsaturated fats, antioxidants | Zucchini: Vitamin C, manganese, antioxidants | Yellow Squash: Vitamin C, antioxidants | Red Bell Pepper: Vitamin C, antioxidants | Red Onion: Quercetin, antioxidants | Cilantro: Vitamin C, flavonoids | Lime: Vitamin C, antioxidants

Ingredients:

For the Salmon:

- 4 salmon fillets (about 6 ounces each) (680g total)
- 1/4 cup honey (84g)
- 2 tablespoons chipotle chili powder (14g)
- 2 tablespoons olive oil (27.2g; 0.96oz)
- 1 tablespoon lime juice (15g; 0.5oz)
- 1 clove garlic, minced (~3g)
- Salt and pepper to taste (~1.5g salt; ~0.6g pepper)

For the Vegetables:

- 2 medium zucchini, sliced into rounds (~240g)
- 2 medium yellow squash, sliced into rounds (~240g)
- 1 red bell pepper, sliced into strips (~120g)
- 1 red onion, sliced (~150g)
- 2 tablespoons olive oil (27.2g; 0.96oz)
- 1 teaspoon garlic powder (3.3g)
- 1 teaspoon dried oregano (1g)
- Salt and pepper to taste (~1.5g salt; ~0.6g pepper)

For Garnish:

- 1/4 cup fresh cilantro, chopped (4g)
- Lime wedges (for serving)

Directions:

Prepare the Honey-Chipotle Marinade:
1. In a small bowl, whisk together the honey, chipotle chili powder, olive oil, lime juice, minced garlic, salt, and pepper.

Marinate the Salmon:
2. Place the salmon fillets on a large plate or shallow dish.
3. Pour the honey-chipotle marinade over the salmon, making sure each fillet is well coated. Let it marinate for at least 15 minutes.

Prepare the Vegetables:
4. In a large bowl, combine the sliced zucchini, yellow squash, red bell pepper, and red onion.
5. Drizzle with olive oil and season with garlic powder, dried oregano, salt, and pepper. Toss to coat the vegetables evenly.

Assemble the Foil Packets:
6. Preheat your grill to medium-high heat.
7. Cut four large pieces of aluminum foil.
8. Place an equal portion of the vegetable mixture in the center of each piece of foil.
9. Place a marinated salmon fillet on top of the vegetables in each packet.
10. Fold the sides of the foil over the salmon and vegetables, sealing the packets well to prevent any leaks.

Grill the Foil Packets:
11. Place the foil packets on the preheated grill.
12. Grill for about 12-15 minutes, or until the salmon is cooked through and flakes easily with a fork, and the vegetables are tender.

Serve:
13. Carefully open the foil packets, being cautious of the hot steam.
14. Garnish with fresh cilantro and serve with lime wedges.

LEMON CHICKEN WITH ASPARAGUS

Time: 45 minutes
Serving size: 4

This simple recipe hits all the marks. Lean protein, antioxidants, healthy fats, vitamins, and anti-inflammatories. Easy, peasy!

Nutritional Information (Approximate per 1 serving):

Calories: 350 kcal | Protein: 30g | Carbohydrates: 8g | Dietary Fiber: 3g |
Sugars: 2g | Fat: 20g | Saturated Fat: 3g | Sodium: 400mg

Beneficial Nutrients & Anti-Inflammatories:

Chicken: Lean protein | Garlic: Allicin, antioxidants | Olive Oil: Monounsaturated fats, antioxidants | Asparagus: Vitamins A, C, E, K, folate, antioxidants | Lemon: Vitamin C, antioxidants | Parsley: Vitamin C, flavonoids

Ingredients:

For the Chicken:

- 4 boneless, skinless chicken breasts (~680g total)
- 2 tablespoons olive oil (27.2g; 0.96oz)
- 1 teaspoon garlic powder (3.3g)
- 1 teaspoon dried thyme (1g)
- 1 teaspoon dried oregano (1g)
- 1/2 teaspoon ground black pepper (1.2g)
- Salt to taste (~1.5g)
- 1 tablespoon lemon zest (6g)
- 2 tablespoons lemon juice (30g; 1.02oz)

For the Asparagus:

- 1 bunch asparagus, trimmed and cut into 2-inch pieces (~300g)
- 1 tablespoon olive oil (13.6g; 0.48oz)
- 2 cloves garlic, minced (~6g)
- Salt and pepper to taste (~1.5g salt; ~0.6g pepper)

For Garnish:

- 1/4 cup fresh parsley, chopped (4g)
- Lemon slices (for serving)

Directions:

Prepare the Chicken:

1. In a small bowl, mix together the olive oil, garlic powder, dried thyme, dried oregano, ground black pepper, salt, lemon zest, and lemon juice.
2. Rub the mixture over the chicken breasts, coating them evenly. Let the chicken marinate for at least 15 minutes.

Cook the Chicken:

3. Heat a large skillet over medium-high heat.
4. Add the marinated chicken breasts to the skillet and cook for about 6-7 minutes per side, or until the internal temperature reaches 165°F (75°C) and the chicken is cooked through.
5. Remove the chicken from the skillet and set aside.

Prepare the Asparagus:

6. In the same skillet, heat the olive oil over medium heat.
7. Add the minced garlic and cook for about 1 minute until fragrant.
8. Add the asparagus pieces, season with salt and pepper, and cook for about 5-7 minutes, stirring occasionally, until the asparagus is tender and slightly charred.

Serve:

9. Slice the cooked chicken breasts and place them on serving plates.
10. Arrange the cooked asparagus alongside the chicken.
11. Garnish with fresh parsley and lemon slices.Lemony Lentil Salad

LOU'S BAKED FISH TACOS WITH TOMATO & AVOCADO SALSA

Time: 30 minutes
Serving size: 2

The inspiration for this one came from a trip I took to San Luis Obispo, California back in the late 2000s, where I witnessed Lou Farrigno (the original Incredible Hulk) in a chicken wing eating contest, while eating the most delicious fish taco I've ever had. It was a moment.

Nutritional Information (Approximate per 1 serving):

Calories: 350 kcal | Protein: 25g | Carbohydrates: 30g | Dietary Fiber: 6g | Sugars: 4g |
Fat: 15g | Saturated Fat: 2g | Sodium: 500mg

Beneficial Nutrients & Anti-Inflammatories:

Fish: Lean protein, omega-3 fatty acids | Tomatoes: Lycopene, vitamin C | Avocado: Monounsaturated fats, vitamin E, antioxidants | Garlic: Allicin, antioxidants | Olive Oil: Monounsaturated fats, antioxidants | Cilantro: Vitamin C, flavonoids | Lime: Vitamin C, antioxidants

Ingredients:

For the Fish Tacos:

- 1 pound white fish fillets (such as cod or haddock), cut into strips (454g)
- 1 cup panko breadcrumbs (50g)
- 1/2 cup cornmeal (70g)
- 1 teaspoon ground cumin (3g)
- 1 teaspoon ground paprika (2.3g)
- 1/2 teaspoon ground black pepper (1.2g)
- 1/2 teaspoon salt (3g)
- 2 large eggs, beaten (100g total)
- 2 tablespoons olive oil (27.2g; 0.96oz)
- 8 small corn tortillas (~192g total)

For the Tomato and Avocado Salsa:

- 2 tomatoes, diced (~240g)
- 1 avocado, diced (~200g)
- 1/4 red onion, finely chopped (~40g)
- 1/4 cup fresh cilantro, chopped (4g)
- 1 tablespoon lime juice (15g; 0.5oz)
- Salt and pepper to taste (~1.5g salt; ~0.6g pepper)

Directions:

Prepare the Salsa:

1. In a medium bowl, combine the diced tomatoes, diced avocado, chopped red onion, fresh cilantro, lime juice, salt, and pepper. Set aside.

Prepare the Fish:

2. Preheat your oven to 400°F (200°C).
3. Line a baking sheet with parchment paper.
4. In a shallow dish, combine the panko breadcrumbs, cornmeal, ground cumin, ground paprika, ground black pepper, and salt.
5. In another shallow dish, beat the eggs.

Coat the Fish:

6. Dip each fish strip into the beaten eggs, then coat with the breadcrumb mixture, pressing gently to adhere.
7. Place the coated fish strips on the prepared baking sheet.

Bake the Fish:

8. Drizzle the fish strips with olive oil.
9. Bake in the preheated oven for 15–20 minutes, or until the fish is golden brown and cooked through, flipping halfway through the baking time.

Assemble the Tacos:

10. Warm the corn tortillas in a dry skillet over medium heat or in the microwave.
11. Place a few pieces of baked fish on each tortilla.
12. Top with the tomato and avocado salsa.

VEGAN QUINOA CHILI WITH SWEET POTATOES

Time: 50 minutes
Serving size: 1/6 of the total dish

You'll make this recipe more than once. More than twice, even. It's chili that's loaded with vegetables, beans, and an incredible blend of spices. It's money.

Nutritional Information (Approximate per 1 serving):

Calories: 350 kcal | Protein: 12g | Carbohydrates: 60g | Dietary Fiber: 14g |
Sugars: 8g | Fat: 8g | Saturated Fat: 1g | Sodium: 600mg

Beneficial Nutrients & Anti-Inflammatories:

Onion: Quercetin, antioxidants | Garlic: Allicin, antioxidants | Sweet Potatoes: Beta-carotene, vitamins A and C | Bell Peppers: Vitamin C, antioxidants | Quinoa: Fiber, magnesium, antioxidants | Black Beans: Fiber, protein, antioxidants | Kidney Beans: Fiber, protein, antioxidants | Tomatoes: Lycopene, vitamin C | Olive Oil: Monounsaturated fats, antioxidants | Cinnamon: Cinnamaldehyde, antioxidants | Cilantro: Vitamin C, flavonoids | Avocado: Monounsaturated fats, vitamin E, antioxidants

Ingredients:

For the Chili:

- 1 tablespoon olive oil (13.6g; 0.48oz)
- 1 large onion, diced (~200g)
- 3 cloves garlic, minced (~9g)
- 1 large sweet potato, peeled and diced (~200g)
- 1 red bell pepper, diced (~120g)
- 1 yellow bell pepper, diced (~120g)
- 1 cup quinoa, rinsed (185g)
- 1 can (15 ounces) black beans, drained and rinsed (425g)
- 1 can (15 ounces) kidney beans, drained and rinsed (425g)
- 1 can (15 ounces) diced tomatoes (425g)
- 4 cups vegetable broth (960g; 33.8oz)

- 2 tablespoons tomato paste (30g)
- 1 tablespoon chili powder (7.5g)
- 2 teaspoons ground cumin (6g)
- 1 teaspoon smoked paprika (2.3g)
- 1/2 teaspoon ground cinnamon (1.3g)
- 1/2 teaspoon ground black pepper (1.2g)
- Salt to taste (~1.5g)
- 1 cup frozen corn kernels (165g)

Directions:

Prepare the Base:

1. In a large pot or Dutch oven, heat the olive oil over medium heat.
2. Add the diced onion and sauté until translucent, about 5 minutes.
3. Add the minced garlic and cook for another minute until fragrant.

Add the Vegetables and Quinoa:

4. Stir in the diced sweet potato, red bell pepper, and yellow bell pepper.
5. Cook for about 5 minutes, stirring occasionally.

Add the Beans and Tomatoes:

6. Add the rinsed quinoa, black beans, kidney beans, diced tomatoes, vegetable broth, and tomato paste to the pot.
7. Stir in the chili powder, ground cumin, smoked paprika, ground cinnamon, ground black pepper, and salt.
8. Bring the mixture to a boil, then reduce the heat to low and let it simmer for about 25–30 minutes, or until the quinoa and sweet potatoes are tender.

Add the Corn:

9. Stir in the frozen corn kernels and cook for an additional 5 minutes.

Serve:

10. Ladle the quinoa chili into bowls.
11. Garnish with fresh cilantro and diced avocado.
12. Serve with lime wedges on the side.

OVEN-ROASTED SALMON WITH CHARRED LEMON VINAIGRETTE

Time: 25 minutes
Serving size: 4

Folks, I've discovered charred lemon and I'm not going back. Whoever invented charred lemon should be given a Nobel prize. It's lemony, but also with a little carmelization. You can swap out the salmon in this recipe for a protein of your choice as well.

Nutritional Information (Approximate per 1 serving):

Calories: 400 kcal | Protein: 30g | Carbohydrates: 8g | Dietary Fiber: 1g |
Sugars: 5g | Fat: 28g | Saturated Fat: 4g | Sodium: 400mg

Beneficial Nutrients & Anti-Inflammatories:

Salmon: Omega-3 fatty acids (EPA and DHA) | Lemon: Vitamin C, antioxidants | Garlic: Allicin, antioxidants | Olive Oil: Monounsaturated fats, antioxidants | Parsley: Vitamin C, flavonoids

Ingredients:

For the Salmon (or a protein of your choice):

- 4 salmon fillets (about 6 ounces each) (680g total)
- 2 tablespoons olive oil (27.2g; 0.96oz)
- 1 teaspoon garlic powder (3.3g)
- 1 teaspoon dried thyme (1g)
- 1 teaspoon ground black pepper (2.3g)
- Salt to taste (~1.5g)

For the Charred Lemon Vinaigrette:

- 2 lemons, halved (~160g total)
- 1/4 cup olive oil (54.4g; 1.92oz)

- 1 tablespoon Dijon mustard (15g)
- 1 tablespoon honey or maple syrup (20g; 0.7oz)
- 1 clove garlic, minced (~3g)
- 1/4 teaspoon ground black pepper (0.6g)
- Salt to taste (~1.5g)
- 2 tablespoons fresh parsley, chopped (4g)

Directions:

Prepare the Salmon (protein):

1. Preheat your oven to 400°F (200°C).
2. Line a baking sheet with parchment paper or lightly grease it.
3. In a small bowl, mix together the olive oil, garlic powder, dried thyme, ground black pepper, and salt.
4. Rub the mixture over the salmon fillets, coating them evenly.
5. Place the salmon fillets on the prepared baking sheet, skin-side down.

Bake the Salmon (protein):

6. Bake in the preheated oven for 12-15 minutes, or until the salmon is cooked through and flakes easily with a fork.

Char the Lemons:

7. While the salmon is baking, heat a dry skillet over medium-high heat.
8. Place the lemon halves cut-side down in the skillet and cook until they are charred and caramelized, about 4-5 minutes.
9. Remove the lemons from the skillet and let them cool slightly.

Prepare the Charred Lemon Vinaigrette:

10. Squeeze the juice from the charred lemons into a small bowl.
11. Add the olive oil, Dijon mustard, honey or maple syrup, minced garlic, ground black pepper, salt, and chopped fresh parsley.
12. Whisk together until well combined.

Serve:

13. Remove the salmon from the oven and transfer to serving plates.
14. Drizzle the charred lemon vinaigrette over the salmon fillets.
15. Garnish with additional fresh parsley if desired.

ROASTED TURMERIC CHICKEN PITAS WITH GARLIC LEMON TAHINI

Time: 35 minutes
Serving size: 4

I call this one a gyro on anti-inflammatory steroids* (*No steroids were used in the creation of this recipe).

Nutritional Information (Approximate per 1 serving):

Calories: 450 kcal | Protein: 35g | Carbohydrates: 30g | Dietary Fiber: 6g | Sugars: 5g |
Fat: 20g | Saturated Fat: 3g | Sodium: 500mg

Beneficial Nutrients & Anti-Inflammatories:

Chicken: Lean protein | Turmeric: Curcumin | Garlic: Allicin, antioxidants | Lemon: Vitamin C, antioxidants | Tahini: Healthy fats, antioxidants | Olive Oil: Monounsaturated fats, antioxidants | Mixed Greens: Vitamins A, C, K, antioxidants | Cherry Tomatoes: Lycopene, vitamin C | Cucumber: Hydration, antioxidants | Red Onion: Quercetin, antioxidants | Parsley: Vitamin C, flavonoids

Ingredients:

For the Chicken:

- 4 boneless, skinless chicken breasts (~680g total)
- 2 tablespoons olive oil (27.2g; 0.96oz)
- 2 teaspoons ground turmeric (6g)
- 1 teaspoon ground cumin (3g)
- 1 teaspoon smoked paprika (2.3g)
- 1/2 teaspoon ground black pepper (1.2g)
- 1/2 teaspoon salt (3g)
- 1 tablespoon lemon juice (15g; 0.5oz)
- 1 tablespoon fresh ginger, grated (6g)

For the Garlic Lemon Tahini Sauce:

- 1/2 cup tahini (120g)
- 2 tablespoons lemon juice (30g; 1.02oz)
- 1/4 cup water (or as needed for desired consistency) (60g; 2.1oz)

- 2 cloves garlic, minced (~6g)
- 1/2 teaspoon ground cumin (1.5g)
- 1/4 teaspoon salt (1.5g)

For the Pitas:

- 4 whole wheat pitas (~240g total)
- 2 cups mixed greens (such as arugula, spinach, and lettuce) (60g)
- 1 cup cherry tomatoes, halved (150g)
- 1 cucumber, sliced (~200g)
- 1/4 red onion, thinly sliced (~40g)
- 1/4 cup fresh parsley, chopped (4g)

Directions:

Prepare the Chicken:

1. Preheat your oven to 400°F (200°C).
2. In a small bowl, mix together the olive oil, ground turmeric, ground cumin, smoked paprika, ground black pepper, salt, lemon juice, and grated fresh ginger.
3. Rub the mixture over the chicken breasts, coating them evenly.
4. Place the chicken breasts on a baking sheet and roast in the preheated oven for 20-25 minutes, or until the internal temperature reaches 165°F (75°C) and the chicken is cooked through.
5. Remove from the oven and let it rest for a few minutes before slicing.

Prepare the Garlic Lemon Tahini Sauce:

6. In a small bowl, whisk together the tahini, lemon juice, water, minced garlic, ground cumin, and salt. Adjust the water quantity to achieve your desired consistency.

Assemble the Pitas:

7. Warm the whole wheat pitas in a dry skillet over medium heat or in the microwave.
8. Cut each pita in half to create pockets.
9. Stuff each pita half with mixed greens, cherry tomatoes, cucumber slices, and thinly sliced red onion.
10. Add slices of the roasted turmeric chicken.

Drizzle and Serve:

11. Drizzle the Garlic Lemon Tahini Sauce over the stuffed pitas.
12. Garnish with chopped fresh parsley.
13. Serve immediately.

ROASTED VEGGIE BUDDHA BOWL

Time: 35 minutes
Serving size: 2

Lord have mercy. This one is delish. I mean, who doesn't love roasted veggies? Add them to a base of healthy quinoa and a great sauce and you have your next food obsession.

Nutritional Information (Approximate per 1 serving):

Calories: 450 kcal | Protein: 12g | Carbohydrates: 55g | Dietary Fiber: 12g | Sugars: 7g | Fat: 20g | Saturated Fat: 3g | Sodium: 600mg

Beneficial Nutrients & Anti-Inflammatories:

Sweet Potato: Beta-carotene, vitamins A and C | Bell Peppers: Vitamin C, antioxidants | Zucchini: Vitamin C, manganese, antioxidants | Red Onion: Quercetin, antioxidants | Quinoa: Fiber, magnesium, antioxidants | Garlic: Allicin, antioxidants | Tahini: Healthy fats, antioxidants | Olive Oil: Monounsaturated fats, antioxidants | Spinach/Mixed Greens: Vitamins A, C, K, antioxidants | Avocado: Monounsaturated fats, vitamin E, antioxidants | Pumpkin/Sunflower Seeds: Vitamin E, healthy fats, antioxidants | Lemon: Vitamin C, antioxidants | Parsley/Cilantro: Vitamin C, flavonoids

Ingredients:

For the Roasted Veggies:
- 1 large sweet potato, peeled and diced (~200g)
- 1 red bell pepper, diced (~120g)
- 1 yellow bell pepper, diced (~120g)
- 1 zucchini, sliced (~200g)
- 1 red onion, sliced (~150g)
- 1 tablespoon olive oil (13.6g; 0.48oz)
- 1 teaspoon ground cumin (3g)
- 1 teaspoon smoked paprika (2.3g)
- 1/2 teaspoon garlic powder (1.6g)
- Salt and pepper to taste (~1.5g salt; ~0.6g pepper)

For the Quinoa:
- 1 cup quinoa, rinsed (185g)
- 2 cups vegetable broth or water (480g; 16.9oz)
- 1/2 teaspoon salt (3g)

For the Tahini Dressing:
- 1/4 cup tahini (60g)
- 2 tablespoons lemon juice (30g; 1.02oz)
- 2 tablespoons water (or as needed for desired consistency) (30g; 1.02oz)
- 1 clove garlic, minced (~3g)
- 1/2 teaspoon ground cumin (1.5g)
- 1/4 teaspoon salt (1.5g)

For the Bowl:
- 2 cups fresh spinach or mixed greens (60g)
- 1 avocado, sliced (~200g)
- 1/4 cup fresh parsley or cilantro, chopped (4g)
- 2 tablespoons pumpkin seeds or sunflower seeds (18g)

Directions:

Prepare the Roasted Veggies:
1. Preheat your oven to 400°F (200°C).
2. In a large bowl, toss the diced sweet potato, red bell pepper, yellow bell pepper, zucchini, and red onion with olive oil, ground cumin, smoked paprika, garlic powder, salt, and pepper.
3. Spread the veggies in a single layer on a baking sheet.
4. Roast in the preheated oven for 20-25 minutes, or until the veggies are tender and slightly caramelized.

Cook the Quinoa:
5. In a medium saucepan, bring the vegetable broth or water to a boil.
6. Add the rinsed quinoa and salt.
7. Reduce the heat to low, cover, and simmer for 15 minutes, or until the quinoa is cooked and the liquid is absorbed.
8. Remove from heat and let it sit, covered, for 5 minutes. Fluff with a fork.

Prepare the Tahini Dressing:
9. In a small bowl, whisk together the tahini, lemon juice, water, minced garlic, ground cumin, and salt. Adjust the water quantity to achieve your desired consistency.

Assemble the Buddha Bowls:
10. Divide the fresh spinach or mixed greens among four bowls.
11. Top each bowl with a portion of cooked quinoa, roasted veggies, sliced avocado, and chopped fresh parsley or cilantro.
12. Sprinkle with pumpkin seeds or sunflower seeds.

Drizzle and Serve:
13. Drizzle the Tahini Dressing over each bowl.
14. Serve immediately.

SAAG TOFU PANEER

Time: 30 minutes
Serving size: 4

A vegetarian powerhouse. My wife and I LOVE Indian cuisine and Saag Paneer never disappoints. This one replaced the paneer cheese with tofu. It works really well. This recipe also happens to be loaded with anti-inflammatory goodies.

Nutritional Information (Approximate per 1 serving):

Calories: 350 kcal | Protein: 20g | Carbohydrates: 20g | Dietary Fiber: 8g | Sugars: 6g | Fat: 14g | Saturated Fat: 3g | Sodium: 450mg

Beneficial Nutrients & Anti-Inflammatories:

Spinach: Vitamins A, C, K, antioxidants | Kale: Vitamins A, C, K, antioxidants | Garlic: Allicin, antioxidants | Ginger: Gingerol, other antioxidants | Turmeric: Curcumin | Olive Oil: Monounsaturated fats, antioxidants | Coconut Milk: Lauric acid, antioxidants | Cumin: Cuminaldehyde, other antioxidants | Coriander: Antioxidants, vitamin C | Garam Masala: Multiple anti-inflammatory spices

Ingredients:

For the Saag:

- 2 tablespoons ghee or coconut oil (27.2g; 0.96oz)
- 1 large onion, diced (~200g)
- 4 cloves garlic, minced (~12g)
- 1 tablespoon fresh ginger, grated (6g)
- 1 teaspoon ground cumin (3g)
- 1 teaspoon ground coriander (1g)
- 1 teaspoon ground turmeric (3g)
- 1/2 teaspoon ground garam masala (1g)
- 1/2 teaspoon ground black pepper (1.2g)
- 1 can (14 ounces) coconut milk (400g)
- 4 cups fresh spinach, chopped (120g)
- 2 cups kale, chopped (60g)
- Salt to taste (~1.5g)

For the Tofu Paneer:

- 1 block (8 ounces) tofu, cubed (227g)
- 1 tablespoon olive oil (13.6g; 0.48oz)

Directions:

Prepare the Paneer:

1. In a large skillet, heat the olive oil over medium heat.
2. Add cubed tofu and cook until golden brown on all sides, about 5-7 minutes. Remove from the skillet and set aside.

Prepare the Saag:

3. In the same skillet, heat the ghee or coconut oil over medium heat.
4. Add the diced onion and sauté until translucent, about 5 minutes.
5. Add the minced garlic and grated ginger, and cook for another minute until fragrant.
6. Stir in the ground cumin, ground coriander, ground turmeric, ground garam masala, and ground black pepper. Cook for another minute.

Add the Greens and Coconut Milk:

7. Add the chopped spinach and kale to the skillet and cook until wilted, about 3-5 minutes.
8. Pour in the coconut milk and bring the mixture to a simmer. Cook for another 5-7 minutes, stirring occasionally.

Blend the Saag (Optional):

9. For a smoother texture, you can use an immersion blender to partially blend the saag, leaving some chunks for texture.
10. Alternatively, you can blend half of the saag in a blender and then return it to the skillet.

Combine the Paneer and Saag:

11. Stir the cooked paneer into the saag and cook for another 2-3 minutes until heated through.

Serve:

12. Serve the saag paneer hot with a side of basmati rice or naan.

SHAWARMA-SEASONED CAULIFLOWER & CHICKPEA PITAS

Time: 40 minutes
Serving size: 2

Shawarma is one of my favorite flavors and if you've never had it, welcome to the world of delightful tastebud sensations. This recipe is vegan, includes loads of anti-inflammatories, and is a go-to in our home.

Nutritional Information (Approximate per 1 serving):

Calories: 450 kcal | Protein: 12g | Carbohydrates: 45g | Dietary Fiber: 12g | Sugars: 6g | Fat: 24g | Saturated Fat: 3g | Sodium: 600mg

Beneficial Nutrients & Anti-Inflammatories:

Cauliflower: Glucosinolates, vitamin C, antioxidants | Chickpeas: Fiber, protein, antioxidants | Garlic: Allicin, antioxidants | Turmeric: Curcumin | Olive Oil: Monounsaturated fats, antioxidants | Tahini: Healthy fats, antioxidants | Lemon: Vitamin C, antioxidants | Mixed Greens: Vitamins A, C, K, antioxidants | Cherry Tomatoes: Lycopene, vitamin C | Cucumber: Hydration, antioxidants | Red Onion: Quercetin, antioxidants | Parsley: Vitamin C, flavonoids

Ingredients:

For the Shawarma-Seasoned Cauliflower and Chickpeas:

- 1 medium head cauliflower, cut into florets (~600g)
- 1 can (15 ounces) chickpeas, drained and rinsed (425g)
- 3 tablespoons olive oil (40.8g; 1.44oz)
- 2 teaspoons ground cumin (6g)
- 2 teaspoons ground coriander (2g)
- 1 teaspoon ground paprika (2.3g)
- 1 teaspoon ground turmeric (3g)
- 1 teaspoon ground cinnamon (2.6g)
- 1/2 teaspoon ground black pepper (1.2g)
- 1/2 teaspoon salt (3g)
- 1/4 teaspoon cayenne pepper (optional) (0.5g)

For the Garlic Lemon Tahini Sauce:

- 1/2 cup tahini (120g)
- 2 tablespoons lemon juice (30g; 1.02oz)
- 1/4 cup water (or as needed for desired consistency) (60g; 2.1oz)
- 2 cloves garlic, minced (~6g)
- 1/2 teaspoon ground cumin (1.5g)
- 1/4 teaspoon salt (1.5g)

For the Pitas:

- 4 whole wheat pitas (~240g total)
- 2 cups mixed greens (such as arugula, spinach, and lettuce) (60g)
- 1 cup cherry tomatoes, halved (150g)
- 1/2 cucumber, sliced (~100g)
- 1/4 red onion, thinly sliced (~40g)
- 1/4 cup fresh parsley, chopped (4g)

....

Directions:

Prepare the Shawarma-Seasoned Cauliflower and Chickpeas:

1. Preheat your oven to 425°F (220°C).
2. In a large bowl, combine the cauliflower florets and chickpeas.
3. Drizzle with olive oil and add ground cumin, ground coriander, ground paprika, ground turmeric, ground cinnamon, ground black pepper, salt, and cayenne pepper (if using). Toss to coat evenly.
4. Spread the mixture in a single layer on a baking sheet.
5. Roast in the preheated oven for 25-30 minutes, stirring halfway through, until the cauliflower is tender and slightly charred, and the chickpeas are crispy.

Prepare the Garlic Lemon Tahini Sauce:

6. In a small bowl, whisk together the tahini, lemon juice, water, minced garlic, ground cumin, and salt. Adjust the water quantity to achieve your desired consistency.

Assemble the Pitas:

7. Warm the whole wheat pitas in a dry skillet over medium heat or in the microwave.
8. Cut each pita in half to create pockets.
9. Stuff each pita half with mixed greens, roasted cauliflower and chickpeas, cherry tomatoes, cucumber slices, and thinly sliced red onion.

Drizzle and Serve:

10. Drizzle the Garlic Lemon Tahini Sauce over the stuffed pitas.
11. Garnish with chopped fresh parsley.
12. Serve immediately.

SHEET PAN CHICKPEA CHICKEN

Time: 45 minutes
Serving size: 4

Anytime you see "sheet pan" on a recipe title, it means "easy to make." You simply put everything on a sheet pan, roast it, and eat. What could be better?

Nutritional Information (Approximate per 1 serving):

Calories: 450 kcal | Protein: 40g | Carbohydrates: 35g | Dietary Fiber: 10g | Sugars: 7g | Fat: 18g | Saturated Fat: 3g | Sodium: 600mg

Beneficial Nutrients & Anti-Inflammatories:

Chicken: Lean protein | Chickpeas: Fiber, protein, antioxidants | Red Bell Pepper: Vitamin C, antioxidants | Yellow Bell Pepper: Vitamin C, antioxidants | Red Onion: Quercetin, antioxidants | Zucchini: Vitamin C, manganese, antioxidants | Garlic: Allicin, antioxidants | Turmeric: Curcumin | Olive Oil: Monounsaturated fats, antioxidants | Lemon: Vitamin C, antioxidants | Dill: Flavonoids, antioxidants | Parsley: Vitamin C, flavonoids

Ingredients:

For the Chicken and Chickpeas:

- 4 boneless, skinless chicken breasts (~680g total)
- 1 can (15 ounces) chickpeas, drained and rinsed (425g)
- 1 red bell pepper, sliced (~120g)
- 1 yellow bell pepper, sliced (~120g)
- 1 red onion, sliced (~150g)
- 1 zucchini, sliced (~200g)
- 2 tablespoons olive oil (27.2g; 0.96oz)
- 2 teaspoons ground cumin (6g)
- 1 teaspoon smoked paprika (2.3g)
- 1 teaspoon ground turmeric (3g)
- 1 teaspoon garlic powder (3.3g)
- 1 teaspoon ground coriander (1g)
- 1/2 teaspoon ground black pepper (1.2g)
- 1/2 teaspoon salt (3g)

- 1 lemon, thinly sliced (~70g)

For the Garlic Lemon Yogurt Sauce:

- 1/2 cup dairy-free yogurt (I use coconut, but you can use any type) (120g)
- 1 tablespoon lemon juice (15g; 0.5oz)
- 1 clove garlic, minced (~3g)
- 1 tablespoon fresh dill, chopped (optional) (3g)
- Salt and pepper to taste (~1.5g salt; ~0.6g pepper)

For Garnish:

- 1/4 cup fresh parsley, chopped (4g)
- Lemon wedges (for serving)

Directions:

Prepare the Chicken and Vegetables:

1. Preheat your oven to 425°F (220°C).
2. In a small bowl, mix together the olive oil, ground cumin, smoked paprika, ground turmeric, garlic powder, ground coriander, ground black pepper, and salt.

Season the Chicken and Vegetables:

3. Place the chicken breasts, chickpeas, red bell pepper, yellow bell pepper, red onion, and zucchini on a large baking sheet.
4. Drizzle the olive oil mixture over the chicken and vegetables. Toss to coat evenly.
5. Arrange the lemon slices on top of the chicken and vegetables.

Roast:

6. Roast in the preheated oven for 25-30 minutes, or until the chicken is cooked through and the vegetables are tender, turning the vegetables halfway through the cooking time.
7. Check that the internal temperature of the chicken reaches 165°F (75°C) using a meat thermometer.

Prepare the Garlic Lemon Yogurt Sauce:

8. In a small bowl, whisk together the Greek yogurt, lemon juice, minced garlic, chopped fresh dill (if using), salt, and pepper. Adjust the seasoning to taste.

Serve:

9. Remove the baking sheet from the oven and transfer the chicken and vegetables to serving plates.
10. Drizzle the Garlic Lemon Yogurt Sauce over the chicken and vegetables.
11. Garnish with fresh parsley and serve with lemon wedges.

SHEET PAN ZUCCHINI CHICKEN MEATBALLS WITH COCONUT CURRY SAUCE

Time: 45 minutes
Serving size: 4

Stop right here. You listening? Look, I'll be honest, we make this recipe probably more than any other in this book. These meatballs are ridiculous. You'll thank me later (by leaving a positive review on Amazon...thanks!)

Nutritional Information (Approximate per 1 serving):

Calories: 450 kcal | Protein: 28g | Carbohydrates: 15g | Dietary Fiber: 4g | Sugars: 5g |
Fat: 32g | Saturated Fat: 18g | Sodium: 750mg

Beneficial Nutrients & Anti-Inflammatories:

Chicken: Lean protein | Zucchini: Vitamin C, manganese, antioxidants | Garlic: Allicin, antioxidants | Turmeric: Curcumin | Olive Oil: Monounsaturated fats, antioxidants | Ginger: Gingerol, other antioxidants | Coconut Milk: Lauric acid, antioxidants | Cilantro: Vitamin C, flavonoids | Lime: Vitamin C, antioxidants

Ingredients:

For the Zucchini Chicken Meatballs:
- 1 pound ground chicken (454g)
- 1 medium zucchini, grated and excess moisture squeezed out (~150g)
- 1/4 cup breadcrumbs (use gluten-free if needed) (30g)
- 1/4 cup grated Parmesan cheese (optional, or use a dairy-free alternative) (25g)
- 1 egg (50g)
- 2 cloves garlic, minced (~6g)
- 1 teaspoon ground cumin (3g)
- 1 teaspoon dried oregano (1g)
- 1/2 teaspoon ground black pepper (1.2g)
- 1/2 teaspoon salt (3g)
- 1/4 cup fresh parsley, chopped (4g)

For the Coconut Curry Sauce:
- 1 tablespoon olive oil (13.6g; 0.48oz)
- 1 onion, finely chopped (~200g)
- 3 cloves garlic, minced (~9g)
- 1 tablespoon fresh ginger, grated (6g)
- 1 tablespoon red curry paste (15g)
- 1 teaspoon ground turmeric (3g)
- 1 teaspoon ground coriander (1g)
- 1 can (14 ounces) coconut milk (400g)
- 1 tablespoon soy sauce or tamari (for gluten-free) (15g; 0.5oz)
- 1 tablespoon lime juice (15g; 0.5oz)
- 1/2 teaspoon salt (3g)
- 1/4 teaspoon ground black pepper (0.6g)

For the Garnish:
- Fresh cilantro, chopped (as needed)
- Lime wedges (for serving)

Directions:

Prepare the Zucchini Chicken Meatballs:
1. Preheat your oven to 400°F (200°C).
2. In a large bowl, combine the ground chicken, grated zucchini, breadcrumbs, grated Parmesan cheese (if using), egg, minced garlic, ground cumin, dried oregano, ground black pepper, salt, and chopped fresh parsley.
3. Mix well until all ingredients are evenly incorporated.
4. Form the mixture into meatballs, about 1 1/2 inches in diameter, and place them on a greased or parchment-lined baking sheet.

Bake the Meatballs:
5. Bake in the preheated oven for 20-25 minutes, or until the meatballs are cooked through and lightly browned.

Prepare the Coconut Curry Sauce:
6. While the meatballs are baking, heat the olive oil in a large skillet over medium heat.
7. Add the chopped onion and sauté until translucent, about 5 minutes.
8. Add the minced garlic and grated ginger, and cook for another minute until fragrant.
9. Stir in the red curry paste, ground turmeric, and ground coriander, and cook for another minute.
10. Pour in the coconut milk, soy sauce or tamari, lime juice, salt, and ground black pepper. Stir to combine.
11. Bring the mixture to a simmer and cook for about 5-7 minutes, allowing the flavors to meld together.

Combine the Meatballs and Sauce:
12. Once the meatballs are done baking, add them to the skillet with the coconut curry sauce.
13. Gently toss the meatballs in the sauce to coat them evenly.
14. Simmer for an additional 5 minutes to allow the meatballs to absorb the flavors of the sauce.

Serve:
15. Serve the meatballs and sauce over a bed of rice, quinoa, or cauliflower rice, if desired.
16. Garnish with chopped fresh cilantro and lime wedges.

SPAGHETTI SQUASH GARLIC NOODLES

Time: 60 minutes
Serving size: 4

Spaghetti squash meet noodle; Noodle meet spaghetti squash. We're doing a lot of match making here, folks. And you thought this was just a cookbook? Think again. And we have another lower-calorie entrée, which is loaded with the anti-inflammatory good stuff.

Nutritional Information (Approximate per 1 serving):

Calories: 200 kcal | Protein: 4g | Carbohydrates: 10g | Dietary Fiber: 5g | Sugars: 9g | Fat: 10g | Saturated Fat: 2g | Sodium: 400mg

Beneficial Nutrients & Anti-Inflammatories:

Spaghetti Squash: Beta-carotene, vitamins A and C | Garlic: Allicin, antioxidants | Olive Oil: Monounsaturated fats, antioxidants | Parsley: Vitamin C, flavonoids | Lemon: Vitamin C, antioxidants

Ingredients:

For the Garlic Noodles:

- 1 large spaghetti squash (~1000g)
- 2 large red peppers (~240g total)
- 3 tablespoons olive oil (40.8g; 1.44oz)
- 6 cloves garlic, minced (~18g)
- 1/4 teaspoon red pepper flakes (optional) (0.5g)
- 1 tablespoon lemon juice (15g; 0.5oz)
- 1 teaspoon lemon zest (2g)

- Salt and pepper to taste (~1.5g salt; ~0.6g pepper)
- 1/4 cup fresh parsley, chopped (4g)

For Garnish:

- Grated Parmesan cheese (optional, or use a dairy-free alternative) (~25g)
- Fresh parsley, chopped (as needed)
- Lemon wedges (for serving)

Directions:

Prepare the Spaghetti Squash & Red Peppers:

1. Preheat your oven to 400°F (200°C).
2. Cut the spaghetti squash in half lengthwise and scoop out the seeds.
3. Drizzle the cut sides with 1 tablespoon of olive oil and season with salt and pepper.
4. Place the squash halves cut-side down on a baking sheet and roast in the preheated oven for 35-40 minutes, or until the flesh is tender and easily shredded with a fork.
5. Cut red peppers into strips and saute in a pan with olive or avocado oil until slightly softened and browned (don't over cook them...think al-dente). When done, remove from heat.
6. Remove squash from the oven and let it cool slightly. Use a fork to scrape the flesh into spaghetti-like strands. Combine with red peppers and set aside.

Make the Garlic Sauce:

7. In a large skillet, heat the remaining 2 tablespoons of olive oil over medium heat.
8. Add the minced garlic and red pepper flakes (if using) and sauté for about 1-2 minutes until fragrant, being careful not to burn the garlic.
9. Stir in the lemon juice, lemon zest, and season with salt and pepper.

Combine and Serve:

10. Add the shredded spaghetti squash and red peppers to the skillet and toss to combine with the garlic sauce. Cook for 2-3 minutes until heated through.
11. Remove from heat and stir in the chopped fresh parsley.
12. Serve immediately, garnished with grated Parmesan cheese (if using), additional parsley, and lemon wedges.

SPICY CHICKEN & SWEET POTATO STEW

Time: 60 minutes
Serving size: 4

A delicious stew made with your choice of protein. I use chicken, but beans or firm tofu would also work well. Hearty and satisfying!

Nutritional Information (Approximate per 1 serving):

Calories: 350 kcal | Protein: 30g | Carbohydrates: 35g | Dietary Fiber: 7g | Sugars: 10g | Fat: 10g | Saturated Fat: 2g | Sodium: 600mg

Beneficial Nutrients & Anti-Inflammatories:

Chicken: Lean protein | Sweet Potatoes: Beta-carotene, vitamins A and C | Garlic: Allicin, antioxidants | Onion: Quercetin, antioxidants | Tomatoes: Lycopene, vitamin C | Turmeric: Curcumin | Olive Oil: Monounsaturated fats, antioxidants | Cilantro: Vitamin C, flavonoids | Ginger: Gingerol, other antioxidants

Ingredients:

For the Stew:

- 1 tablespoon olive oil (13.6g; 0.48oz)
- 1 pound boneless, skinless chicken breasts, cut into bite-sized pieces (or your choice of protein) (454g)
- 1 large onion, diced (~200g)
- 3 cloves garlic, minced (~9g)
- 1 tablespoon fresh ginger, grated (6g)
- 1 large sweet potato, peeled and diced (~200g)
- 1 red bell pepper, diced (~120g)
- 1 can (14.5 ounces) diced tomatoes (411g)
- 4 cups chicken broth (960g; 33.8oz)
- 1 tablespoon tomato paste (15g)
- 1 tablespoon ground cumin (6g)
- 1 tablespoon ground coriander (1g)
- 1 teaspoon ground turmeric (3g)
- 1/2 teaspoon ground cinnamon (1.3g)
- 1/2 teaspoon ground black pepper (1.2g)
- 1/2 teaspoon red pepper flakes (adjust to taste) (0.5g)
- 1/2 teaspoon salt (adjust to taste) (3g)
- 1/4 cup fresh cilantro, chopped (4g)

For Garnish:

- Fresh cilantro, chopped (as needed)
- Lime wedges (for serving)

Directions:

Prepare the Stew:

1. In a large pot or Dutch oven, heat the olive oil over medium heat.
2. Add the diced chicken and cook until browned on all sides, about 5-7 minutes. Remove the chicken from the pot and set aside.
3. In the same pot, add the diced onion and sauté until translucent, about 5 minutes.
4. Add the minced garlic and grated ginger, and cook for another minute until fragrant.

Add the Vegetables and Spices:

5. Stir in the diced sweet potato and red bell pepper, and cook for 3-4 minutes.
6. Add the diced tomatoes, chicken broth, and tomato paste. Stir to combine.
7. Stir in the ground cumin, ground coriander, ground turmeric, ground cinnamon, ground black pepper, red pepper flakes, and salt.

Cook the Stew:

8. Bring the mixture to a boil, then reduce the heat to low and let it simmer for about 20 minutes, or until the sweet potatoes are tender.
9. Return the cooked chicken to the pot and simmer for an additional 10 minutes, allowing the flavors to meld together.

Serve:

10. Stir in the chopped fresh cilantro.
11. Serve the spicy chicken and sweet potato stew in bowls, garnished with additional cilantro and lime wedges.

SPRING CHICKEN WITH ARTICHOKES & ASPARAGUS

Time: 45 minutes
Serving size: 4

I'm not a spring chicken anymore. But this recipe sure is! (sorry, terrible dad joke) You're going to love this one. It includes artichoke, a little white wine, garlic, lemon...just to name a few goodies. A very delicious dish you're sure to enjoy more than once.

Nutritional Information (Approximate per 1 serving):

Calories: 350 kcal | Protein: 35g | Carbohydrates: 10g | Dietary Fiber: 6g |
Sugars: 4g | Fat: 18g | Saturated Fat: 3g | Sodium: 500mg

Beneficial Nutrients & Anti-Inflammatories:

Chicken: Lean protein | Artichokes: Fiber, vitamin C, antioxidants | Asparagus: Vitamins A, C, K, folate, antioxidants | Garlic: Allicin, antioxidants | Lemon: Vitamin C, antioxidants | Olive Oil: Monounsaturated fats, antioxidants | Parsley: Vitamin C, flavonoids

Ingredients:

For the Spring Chicken:

- 4 boneless, skinless chicken breasts (~680g total)
- 2 tablespoons olive oil (27.2g; 0.96oz)
- 1 large onion, diced (~200g)
- 3 cloves garlic, minced (~9g)
- 1 can (14 ounces) artichoke hearts, drained and quartered (396g)
- 1 bunch asparagus, trimmed and cut into 2-inch pieces (~300g)
- 1/2 cup low-sodium chicken broth (120g; 4.2oz)
- 1/4 cup dry white wine (optional, can replace with additional chicken broth) (60g; 2.1oz)
- 1 tablespoon lemon juice (15g; 0.5oz)
- 1 teaspoon lemon zest (2g)
- 1 teaspoon dried thyme (1g)
- 1 teaspoon dried oregano (1g)
- 1/2 teaspoon ground black pepper (1.2g)
- 1/2 teaspoon salt (adjust to taste) (3g)
- 1/4 cup fresh parsley, chopped (4g)

For Garnish:

- Fresh parsley, chopped (as needed)
- Lemon wedges (for serving)

Directions:

Prepare the Chicken:

1. Season the chicken breasts with salt, pepper, dried thyme, and dried oregano.
2. In a large skillet, heat 1 tablespoon of olive oil over medium-high heat.
3. Add the chicken breasts and cook for about 5-7 minutes per side, or until golden brown and cooked through. Remove the chicken from the skillet and set aside.

Prepare the Vegetables:

4. In the same skillet, add the remaining tablespoon of olive oil.
5. Add the diced onion and sauté until translucent, about 5 minutes.
6. Add the minced garlic and cook for another minute until fragrant.

Combine the Ingredients:

7. Add the artichoke hearts and asparagus to the skillet, and cook for about 3-4 minutes until the asparagus is tender-crisp.
8. Pour in the chicken broth, white wine (if using), lemon juice, and lemon zest. Stir to combine.
9. Return the cooked chicken breasts to the skillet and simmer for 5-7 minutes, allowing the flavors to meld together.

Serve:

10. Transfer the chicken and vegetables to serving plates.
11. Spoon the sauce over the chicken and vegetables.
12. Garnish with chopped fresh parsley and lemon wedges.

SUPERFOOD GRAIN BOWLS

Time: 40 minutes
Serving size:
1/4 of the total dish per serving

Okay, so the term "superfood" is a marketing term. Now you know. However, it is an effective marketing term because it generally describes foods that are packed with beneficial nutrients. This recipe includes several "superfoods" such as quinoa, sweet potato, kale, avocado, blueberries, and olive oil. You can also add more superfoods to this recipe. I kept it simple, but feel free to experiment!

Nutritional Information (Approximate per 1 serving):

Calories: 400 kcal | Protein: 14g | Carbohydrates: 55g | Dietary Fiber: 12g | Sugars: 10g | Fat: 15g | Saturated Fat: 2g | Sodium: 500mg

Beneficial Nutrients & Anti-Inflammatories:

Quinoa: Fiber, protein, antioxidants | Sweet Potatoes: Beta-carotene, vitamins A and C | Kale: Vitamins A, C, K, antioxidants | Avocado: Monounsaturated fats, vitamin E, antioxidants | Blueberries: Anthocyanins, vitamin C | Pumpkin Seeds: Zinc, magnesium, antioxidants | Olive Oil: Monounsaturated fats, antioxidants | Lemon: Vitamin C, antioxidants | Turmeric: Curcumin

Ingredients:

For the Grain Bowls:

- 1 cup quinoa, rinsed (185g)
- 2 cups water or vegetable broth (480g; 16.9oz)
- 1 large sweet potato, peeled and diced (~200g)
- 1 tablespoon olive oil (13.6g; 0.48oz)
- 2 cups kale, chopped (60g)
- 1 avocado, sliced (~200g)
- 1/2 cup blueberries (75g)
- 1/4 cup pumpkin seeds (35g)

For the Turmeric Lemon Dressing:

- 1/4 cup olive oil (54.4g; 1.92oz)
- 2 tablespoons lemon juice (30g; 1.02oz)
- 1 tablespoon apple cider vinegar (15g; 0.5oz)
- 1 tablespoon maple syrup (20g; 0.7oz)
- 1 teaspoon ground turmeric (3g)
- 1 clove garlic, minced (~3g)
- Salt and pepper to taste (~1.5g salt; ~0.6g pepper)

Directions:

Prepare the Quinoa:

1. In a medium saucepan, bring 2 cups of water or vegetable broth to a boil.
2. Add the rinsed quinoa, reduce the heat to low, cover, and simmer for about 15 minutes, or until the liquid is absorbed and the quinoa is tender.
3. Remove from heat and let it sit, covered, for 5 minutes. Fluff with a fork and set aside.

Roast the Sweet Potatoes:

4. Preheat your oven to 400°F (200°C).
5. Toss the diced sweet potatoes with 1 tablespoon of olive oil, and season with salt and pepper.
6. Spread the sweet potatoes on a baking sheet in a single layer.
7. Roast in the preheated oven for 20 minutes, or until tender and slightly caramelized.

Prepare the Kale:

8. While the sweet potatoes are roasting, massage the chopped kale with a small amount of olive oil and a pinch of salt until it becomes tender and dark green. Set aside.

Prepare the Turmeric Lemon Dressing:

9. In a small bowl, whisk together the olive oil, lemon juice, apple cider vinegar, maple syrup, ground turmeric, minced garlic, salt, and pepper. Adjust the seasoning to taste.

Assemble the Bowls:

10. Divide the cooked quinoa among four bowls.
11. Top each bowl with roasted sweet potatoes, massaged kale, avocado slices, blueberries, and pumpkin seeds.
12. Drizzle the turmeric lemon dressing over each bowl.

SWEET POTATO & BEAN ENCHILADAS

Time: 25 minutes
Serving size: 2

Another go-to in our home. This one calls for enchilada sauce. Now, I'm no fool. Those that know good enchilada sauce have their favorites, and I was not about to mess with a good thing. So, you're encouraged to buy your favorite sauce for this one or make your Abuela's time-tested recipe. If I were you, I would go with the latter.

Nutritional Information (Approximate per 1 serving):

Calories: 350 kcal | Protein: 10g | Carbohydrates: 58g | Dietary Fiber: 12g |
Sugars: 6g | Fat: 10g | Saturated Fat: 1.5g | Sodium: 600mg

Beneficial Nutrients & Anti-Inflammatories:

Sweet Potatoes: Beta-carotene, vitamins A and C | Black Beans: Fiber, protein, antioxidants | Garlic: Allicin, antioxidants | Turmeric: Curcumin | Avocado: Monounsaturated fats, vitamin E, antioxidants | Olive Oil: Monounsaturated fats, antioxidants | Cilantro: Vitamin C, flavonoids

....

Ingredients:

For the Enchiladas:

- 2 medium sweet potatoes, peeled and diced (~400g)
- 1 can (15 ounces) black beans, drained and rinsed (425g)
- 1 cup corn kernels (fresh or frozen) (165g)
- 1/2 red onion, finely chopped (~60g)
- 2 cloves garlic, minced (~6g)
- 1 teaspoon ground cumin (3g)
- 1 teaspoon ground paprika (2.3g)
- 1 teaspoon ground turmeric (3g)

- Salt and pepper to taste (~1.5g salt; ~0.6g pepper)
- 8 whole wheat tortillas (~320g total)
- 1 cup enchilada sauce (store-bought or homemade) (240g)
- 1/2 cup vegan cheese (optional) (60g)

For the Toppings:

- 1 avocado, diced (~200g)
- 1/4 cup fresh cilantro, chopped (4g)
- 1 lime, cut into wedges (~70g)

....

Directions:

Prepare the Filling:

1. Preheat your oven to 375°F (190°C).
2. In a large skillet, heat 1 tablespoon of olive oil over medium heat.
3. Add the diced sweet potatoes and cook for about 8–10 minutes until tender.
4. Add the black beans, corn, red onion, garlic, ground cumin, ground paprika, ground turmeric, salt, and pepper. Cook for another 5 minutes until well combined and heated through.

Assemble the Enchiladas:

5. Spread a thin layer of enchilada sauce at the bottom of a baking dish.
6. Place a tortilla on a flat surface and spoon the sweet potato and bean mixture down the center.
7. Roll up the tortilla and place it seam-side down in the baking dish. Repeat with remaining tortillas and filling.
8. Pour the remaining enchilada sauce over the rolled tortillas and sprinkle with vegan cheese (if using).

Bake:

9. Bake in the preheated oven for 10 minutes, until heated through and the cheese (if using) is melted.

SWEET POTATO LENTIL CURRY

Time: 60 minutes
Serving size:
1/4 of the total dish per serving

Hearty, satisfying, and downright comforting. Perfect for a cold day. Packed full of beneficial nutrients!

Nutritional Information (Approximate per 1 serving):

Calories: 350 kcal | Protein: 12g | Carbohydrates: 55g | Dietary Fiber: 15g |

Sugars: 12g | Fat: 8g | Saturated Fat: 3g | Sodium: 600mg

Beneficial Nutrients & Anti-Inflammatories:

Sweet Potatoes: Beta-carotene, vitamins A and C | Lentils: Fiber, protein, antioxidants | Garlic: Allicin, antioxidants | Ginger: Gingerol, other antioxidants | Turmeric: Curcumin | Coconut Milk: Lauric acid, antioxidants | Tomatoes: Lycopene, vitamin C | Spinach: Vitamins A, C, K, antioxidants | Olive Oil: Monounsaturated fats, antioxidants | Cilantro: Vitamin C, flavonoids

Ingredients:

For the Curry:

- 1 tablespoon olive oil (13.6g; 0.48oz)
- 1 large onion, diced (~200g)
- 3 cloves garlic, minced (~9g)
- 1 tablespoon fresh ginger, grated (6g)
- 1 large sweet potato, peeled and diced (~400g)
- 1 cup dried red lentils, rinsed (200g)
- 1 can (14.5 ounces) diced tomatoes (411g)
- 1 can (14 ounces) coconut milk (400g)
- 4 cups vegetable broth (960g; 33.8oz)
- 1 tablespoon curry powder (6g)

- 1 teaspoon ground cumin (3g)
- 1 teaspoon ground turmeric (3g)
- 1/2 teaspoon ground cinnamon (1.3g)
- 1/2 teaspoon ground black pepper (1.2g)
- 1/2 teaspoon salt (adjust to taste) (3g)
- 3 cups fresh spinach, chopped (90g)

For Garnish:

- Fresh cilantro, chopped (as needed)
- Lime wedges (for serving)

Directions:

Prepare the Curry:
1. In a large pot or Dutch oven, heat the olive oil over medium heat.
2. Add the diced onion and sauté until translucent, about 5 minutes.
3. Add the minced garlic and grated ginger, and cook for another minute until fragrant.

Add the Vegetables and Lentils:
4. Stir in the diced sweet potato and cook for 3-4 minutes.
5. Add the rinsed lentils, diced tomatoes, coconut milk, and vegetable broth. Stir to combine.
6. Stir in the curry powder, ground cumin, ground turmeric, ground cinnamon, ground black pepper, and salt.

Cook the Curry:
7. Bring the mixture to a boil, then reduce the heat to low and let it simmer for about 25-30 minutes, or until the sweet potatoes and lentils are tender and the flavors have melded together.
8. Stir in the chopped spinach and cook for an additional 5 minutes, until the spinach is wilted.

Serve:
9. Serve the sweet potato lentil curry in bowls.
10. Garnish with chopped fresh cilantro and lime wedges.

TOFU & MUSHROOM LARB

Time: 35 minutes
Serving size:
1/4 of the total dish per serving

Larb is a traditional Thai dish typically made of ground meat and lots of fresh herbs such as mint, cilantro, and green onions. It's absolutely delicious. I've had this very (very) spicy in the past. I won't subject you to that level of heat (feel free to add heat as you desire), but I will subject you to the rest of the recipe's goodness. Trust me, you'll come back to this one!

Nutritional Information (Approximate per 1 serving):

Calories: 200 kcal | Protein: 10g | Carbohydrates: 15g | Dietary Fiber: 5g | Sugars: 6g | Fat: 12g | Saturated Fat: 1.5g | Sodium: 500mg

Beneficial Nutrients & Anti-Inflammatories:

Tofu: Plant-based protein, isoflavones | Mushrooms: Beta-glucans, antioxidants | Garlic: Allicin, antioxidants | Ginger: Gingerol, other antioxidants | Olive Oil: Monounsaturated fats, antioxidants | Cilantro: Vitamin C, flavonoids | Lime: Vitamin C, antioxidants | Mint: Rosmarinic acid, antioxidants | Red Onion: Quercetin, antioxidants

Ingredients:

For the Larb:

- 1 tablespoon olive oil (13.6g; 0.48oz)
- 1 block (14 ounces) firm tofu, crumbled (396g)
- 2 cups mushrooms, finely chopped (~150g)
- 1 large red onion, thinly sliced (~200g)
- 3 cloves garlic, minced (~9g)
- 1 tablespoon fresh ginger, grated (6g)
- 1 red chili, finely chopped (optional, for heat) (~10g)
- 2 tablespoons soy sauce or tamari (for gluten-free) (30g; 1.02oz)
- 2 tablespoons lime juice (30g; 1.02oz)
- 1 tablespoon fish sauce (optional) (15g; 0.5oz)

- 1 tablespoon maple syrup (20g; 0.7oz)
- 1/4 cup fresh cilantro, chopped (4g)
- 1/4 cup fresh mint, chopped (4g)
- 2 green onions, thinly sliced (~30g)

For Serving:

- (Option 1) 1 head butter lettuce or romaine lettuce, leaves separated (~200g)
- (Option 2) 1 cup jasmine rice (185g)
- 1/4 cup roasted peanuts, chopped (optional) (30g)
- Lime wedges (for serving) (~70g)

Directions:

Prepare the Larb:

1. In a large skillet, heat the olive oil over medium heat.
2. Add the crumbled tofu and cook for about 5 minutes until it starts to brown slightly.
3. Add the chopped mushrooms and cook for another 5 minutes until they release their moisture and start to brown.
4. Add the sliced red onion, minced garlic, grated ginger, and chopped red chili (if using). Cook for 2-3 minutes until the onions soften.
5. If you're serving this with jasmine rice, follow the directions on the rice package and cook rice. Normally it takes about 20 minutes.

Add the Seasonings:

6. Stir in the soy sauce/tamari, lime juice, fish sauce (if using), and maple syrup. Cook for another 2-3 minutes until everything is well combined and heated through.

Finish the Larb:

7. Remove the skillet from heat and stir in the chopped cilantro, mint, and green onions.

Serve:

8. (option 1) Spoon the tofu and mushroom larb into lettuce leaves to create wraps.
9. (option 2) Serve the larb over or on the side of cooked jasmine rice
10. Sprinkle with chopped roasted peanuts (if using) and serve with lime wedges on the side.

TOMATO BASIL GARLIC CHICKEN

Time: 40 minutes
Serving size:
1/4 of the total dish per serving

A simple recipe with a simple tomato basil sauce that's easy to make. Tomatoes (which are loaded with lycopene) are an anti-inflammatory powerhouse. **Here's a power tip:** Crushing or finely dicing tomatoes helps liberate the lycopene from the cell walls of the tomato where it is bound to fiber. I'll bet you didn't know that! Or maybe you did. Whatever. Just make this recipe. Its delicious.

Nutritional Information (Approximate per 1 serving):

Calories: 320 kcal | Protein: 30g | Carbohydrates: 10g | Dietary Fiber: 3g | Sugars: 6g | Fat: 18g | Saturated Fat: 3g | Sodium: 450mg

Beneficial Nutrients & Anti-Inflammatories:

Chicken: Lean protein | Tomatoes: Lycopene, vitamin C | Garlic: Allicin, antioxidants | Olive Oil: Monounsaturated fats, antioxidants | Basil: Eucalyptol, antioxidants

Ingredients:

For the Chicken:

- 4 boneless, skinless chicken breasts (~680g total)
- 2 tablespoons olive oil (27.2g; 0.96oz)
- Salt and pepper to taste (~1.5g salt; ~0.6g pepper)

For the Tomato Basil Garlic Sauce:

- 3 tablespoons olive oil (40.8g; 1.44oz)
- 6 cloves garlic, minced (~18g)
- 1 pint cherry tomatoes, halved (~300g)
- 1 can (14.5 ounces) diced tomatoes (411g)

- 1/2 teaspoon red pepper flakes (optional, for heat) (0.5g)
- 1/4 cup fresh basil, chopped (5g)
- 1 tablespoon balsamic vinegar (15g; 0.5oz)
- Salt and pepper to taste (~1.5g salt; ~0.6g pepper)

For Garnish:

- Fresh basil leaves (as needed)
- Grated Parmesan cheese (optional, or use a dairy-free alternative) (~25g)

Directions:

Prepare the Chicken:

1. Preheat your oven to 375°F (190°C).
2. Season the chicken breasts with salt and pepper.
3. In a large oven-safe skillet, heat 2 tablespoons of olive oil over medium-high heat.
4. Add the chicken breasts and sear for 3-4 minutes on each side until golden brown. Remove the chicken from the skillet and set aside.

Prepare the Tomato Basil Garlic Sauce:

5. In the same skillet, add 3 tablespoons of olive oil and reduce the heat to medium.
6. Add the minced garlic and sauté for about 1 minute until fragrant.
7. Add the cherry tomatoes and cook for 3-4 minutes until they start to soften.
8. Stir in the diced tomatoes, red pepper flakes (if using), chopped basil, balsamic vinegar, salt, and pepper. Cook for another 5 minutes until the sauce thickens slightly.

Combine and Bake:

9. Return the seared chicken breasts to the skillet, nestling them into the tomato basil garlic sauce.
10. Spoon some of the sauce over the chicken.
11. Transfer the skillet to the preheated oven and bake for 20 minutes, or until the chicken is cooked through and reaches an internal temperature of 165°F (75°C).

Serve:

12. Remove the skillet from the oven and let the chicken rest for a few minutes.
13. Serve the chicken with the tomato basil garlic sauce spooned over the top.
14. Garnish with fresh basil leaves and grated Parmesan cheese (if using).

VEGAN BURRITO BOWLS WITH CAULIFLOWER RICE

Time: 40 minutes
Serving size:
1/4 of the total dish per serving

If you like corn salsa and Pico de Gallo, and you like flavor, you'll love this dish. We make this one quite often!

Nutritional Information (Approximate per 1 serving):

Calories: 300 kcal | Protein: 10g | Carbohydrates: 35g | Dietary Fiber: 10g | Sugars: 8g | Fat: 14g | Saturated Fat: 2g | Sodium: 600mg

Beneficial Nutrients & Anti-Inflammatories:

Cauliflower: Vitamin C, fiber, antioxidants | Black Beans: Fiber, protein, antioxidants | Avocado: Monounsaturated fats, vitamin E, antioxidants | Tomatoes: Lycopene, vitamin C | Red Onion: Quercetin, antioxidants | Garlic: Allicin, antioxidants | Olive Oil: Monounsaturated fats, antioxidants | Cilantro: Vitamin C, flavonoids | Lime: Vitamin C, antioxidants

Ingredients:

For the Cauliflower Rice:
- 1 large head of cauliflower, grated or processed into rice-sized pieces (~600g)
- 1 tablespoon olive oil (13.6g; 0.48oz)
- 2 cloves garlic, minced (~6g)
- Salt and pepper to taste (~1.5g salt; ~0.6g pepper)

For the Black Beans:
- 1 can (15 ounces) black beans, drained and rinsed (425g)
- 1 teaspoon ground cumin (3g)
- 1 teaspoon chili powder (2.6g)
- 1/2 teaspoon ground black pepper (1.2g)
- 1/2 teaspoon salt (3g)

For the Corn Salsa:
- 1 cup corn kernels (fresh or frozen) (165g)
- 1/2 red bell pepper, diced (~60g)
- 1/4 red onion, finely chopped (~40g)
- 1/4 cup fresh cilantro, chopped (4g)
- 1 tablespoon lime juice (15g; 0.5oz)
- Salt and pepper to taste (~1.5g salt; ~0.6g pepper)

For the Pico de Gallo:
- 2 tomatoes, diced (~240g)
- 1/4 red onion, finely chopped (~40g)
- 1 jalapeño, finely chopped (optional) (~15g)
- 1/4 cup fresh cilantro, chopped (4g)
- 1 tablespoon lime juice (15g; 0.5oz)
- Salt and pepper to taste (~1.5g salt; ~0.6g pepper)

For the Avocado Crema:
- 1 avocado (~200g)
- 1/4 cup dairy-free yogurt (60g)
- 1 tablespoon lime juice (15g; 0.5oz)
- 1 clove garlic, minced (~3g)
- Salt and pepper to taste (~1.5g salt; ~0.6g pepper)

For the Bowls:
- 2 cups mixed greens (such as arugula, spinach, and lettuce) (60g)
- 1/4 cup fresh cilantro, chopped (4g)
- Lime wedges (for serving) (~70g)

Directions:

Prepare the Cauliflower Rice:
1. In a large skillet, heat the olive oil over medium heat.
2. Add the minced garlic and sauté for about 1 minute until fragrant.
3. Add the grated cauliflower and season with salt and pepper.
4. Cook for 5-7 minutes, stirring occasionally, until the cauliflower is tender. Remove from heat and set aside.

Prepare the Black Beans:
5. In a medium saucepan, add the black beans, ground cumin, chili powder, ground black pepper, and salt.
6. Cook over medium heat for 5-7 minutes until heated through. Remove from heat and set aside.

Prepare the Corn Salsa:
7. In a medium bowl, combine the corn kernels, diced red bell pepper, finely chopped red onion, chopped cilantro, lime juice, salt, and pepper.
8. Mix well and set aside.

Prepare the Pico de Gallo:
9. In a medium bowl, combine the diced tomatoes, finely chopped red onion, finely chopped jalapeño (if using), chopped cilantro, lime juice, salt, and pepper.
10. Mix well and set aside.

Prepare the Avocado Crema:
11. In a small bowl, mash the avocado with a fork.
12. Stir in the dairy-free yogurt, lime juice, minced garlic, salt, and pepper until smooth and creamy. Set aside.

Assemble the Bowls:
13. Divide the cauliflower rice among four bowls.
14. Top each bowl with mixed greens, black beans, corn salsa, pico de gallo, and a dollop of avocado crema.
15. Garnish with chopped fresh cilantro and lime wedges.

WALNUT-ROSEMARY CRUSTED (PROTEIN)

Time: 35 minutes
Serving size: 4

If you enjoy eating nuts, walnuts are among the most anti-inflammatory because they include high levels of alpha-linolenic acid (ALA), an omega-3 fatty acid that is important for reducing inflammation. Including walnuts to any recipe will significantly increase its anti-inflammatory benefits.

Nutritional Information (Approximate per 1 serving):

Calories: 450 kcal | Protein: 30g | Carbohydrates: 8g | Dietary Fiber: 2g |
Sugars: 2g | Fat: 34g | Saturated Fat: 5g | Sodium: 400mg

Beneficial Nutrients & Anti-Inflammatories:

Salmon: Omega-3 fatty acids (EPA and DHA), lean protein | Walnuts: Omega-3 fatty acids (alpha-linolenic acid), antioxidants | Garlic: Allicin, antioxidants | Olive Oil: Monounsaturated fats, antioxidants | Rosemary: Rosmarinic acid, antioxidants | Lemon: Vitamin C, antioxidants

Ingredients:

For the Salmon (or a Protein of Your Choice):
- 4 salmon fillets (about 6 ounces each) (680g total)
- 1 tablespoon olive oil (13.6g; 0.48oz)
- Salt and pepper to taste (~1.5g salt; ~0.6g pepper)

For the Walnut-Rosemary Crust:
- 1 cup walnuts, finely chopped (120g)
- 1/4 cup breadcrumbs (use gluten-free if needed) (30g)

- 2 tablespoons fresh rosemary, chopped (3g)
- 2 cloves garlic, minced (~6g)
- 1 tablespoon lemon zest (6g)
- 2 tablespoons olive oil (27.2g; 0.96oz)
- 1 tablespoon Dijon mustard (15g)
- Salt and pepper to taste (~1.5g salt; ~0.6g pepper)

For Garnish:
- Lemon wedges (for serving) (~70g)
- Fresh rosemary sprigs (as needed)

Directions:

Prepare the Salmon (protein):

1. Preheat your oven to 400°F (200°C).
2. Place the salmon fillets on a baking sheet lined with parchment paper.
3. Drizzle the salmon with 1 tablespoon of olive oil and season with salt and pepper.

Prepare the Walnut-Rosemary Crust:

4. In a medium bowl, combine the finely chopped walnuts, breadcrumbs, chopped fresh rosemary, minced garlic, lemon zest, olive oil, and Dijon mustard. Mix until well combined.
5. Season the mixture with salt and pepper to taste.

Crust the Salmon (protein):

6. Spoon the walnut-rosemary mixture evenly over the top of each salmon fillet, pressing it down gently to adhere to the fish.

Bake the Salmon:

7. Bake the crusted salmon in the preheated oven for 15-20 minutes, or until the salmon is cooked through and the crust is golden brown.

Serve:

8. Remove the salmon from the oven and let it rest for a few minutes.

WALNUT SAGE PESTO PASTA WITH DELICATA SQUASH

Time: 45 minutes
Serving size:
1/4 of the total dish per serving

For those that don't know, delicata squash are the smaller yellow ones with the stripes. I had to figure that out the hard way. This one is another "superfood" recipe (most of the recipes in this book are "superfood" recipes, by the way), and is easy to make. Enjoy!

Nutritional Information (Approximate per 1 serving):

Calories: 500 kcal | Protein: 14g | Carbohydrates: 60g | Dietary Fiber: 8g |
Sugars: 6g | Fat: 24g | Saturated Fat: 3g | Sodium: 450mg

Beneficial Nutrients & Anti-Inflammatories:

Walnuts: Omega-3 fatty acids (alpha-linolenic acid), antioxidants | Sage: Rosmarinic acid, antioxidants | Garlic: Allicin, antioxidants | Olive Oil: Monounsaturated fats, antioxidants | Delicata Squash: Beta-carotene, vitamins A and C | Lemon: Vitamin C, antioxidants

Ingredients:

For the Walnut Sage Pesto:
- 1 cup walnuts (120g)
- 1/2 cup fresh sage leaves (10g)
- 1/2 cup fresh parsley (8g)
- 2 cloves garlic (~6g)
- 1/2 cup olive oil (108.8g; 3.84oz)
- 1/4 cup nutritional yeast (or grated Parmesan cheese if not vegan) (20g)
- 2 tablespoons lemon juice (30g; 1.02oz)
- Salt and pepper to taste (~1.5g salt; ~0.6g pepper)

For the Pasta:
- 12 ounces gluten-free pasta (I really like Jovial's gluten-free pasta) (340g)
- 2 small delicata squashes, halved, seeded, and sliced into 1/2-inch rings (~500g total)
- 2 tablespoons olive oil (27.2g; 0.96oz)
- Salt and pepper to taste (~1.5g salt; ~0.6g pepper)

For Garnish:
- Fresh parsley, chopped (as needed)
- Lemon wedges (for serving) (~70g)

Directions:

Prepare the Walnut Sage Pesto:
1. In a food processor, combine the walnuts, fresh sage leaves, fresh parsley, garlic, nutritional yeast (or Parmesan cheese), lemon juice, salt, and pepper.
2. Pulse until the mixture is finely chopped.
3. With the food processor running, slowly pour in the olive oil until the pesto is smooth and well combined.
4. Adjust the seasoning with additional salt, pepper, or lemon juice to taste.

Prepare the Delicata Squash:
5. Preheat your oven to 400°F (200°C).
6. Toss the sliced delicata squash with 2 tablespoons of olive oil, salt, and pepper.
7. Spread the squash in a single layer on a baking sheet.
8. Roast in the preheated oven for 20-25 minutes, or until the squash is tender and lightly caramelized, turning halfway through.

Cook the Pasta:
9. While the squash is roasting, bring a large pot of salted water to a boil.
10. Add the pasta and cook according to package instructions until al dente.
11. Drain the pasta, reserving 1/2 cup of the pasta cooking water.

Combine and Serve:
12. In a large bowl, toss the cooked pasta with the walnut sage pesto, adding the reserved pasta cooking water as needed to create a creamy sauce.
13. Gently fold in the roasted delicata squash.
14. Divide the pasta among four bowls.
15. Garnish with chopped fresh parsley and serve with lemon wedges.

WHITE BEAN & SUN-DRIED TOMATO GNOCCHI

Time: 35 minutes
Serving size:
1/4 of the total dish per serving

I absolutely love this recipe. The sauce is really tasty. Gnocchi are tricky little devils. They look small, but they fill you up fast. Definitely prioritize gluten-free varieties if you can find them. Otherwise, a regular potato gnocchi should do the trick.

Nutritional Information (Approximate per 1 serving):

Calories: 400 kcal | Protein: 14g | Carbohydrates: 55g | Dietary Fiber: 10g |
Sugars: 8g | Fat: 14g | Saturated Fat: 2g | Sodium: 700mg

Beneficial Nutrients & Anti-Inflammatories:

White Beans: Fiber, protein, antioxidants | Sun-Dried Tomatoes: Lycopene, vitamin C | Garlic: Allicin, antioxidants |
Olive Oil: Monounsaturated fats, antioxidants | Spinach: Vitamins A, C, K, antioxidants | Basil: Eucalyptol, antioxidants

Ingredients:

For the Gnocchi:

- 1 package (16 ounces) potato gnocchi (use gluten-free if needed) (454g)
- 1 tablespoon olive oil (13.6g; 0.48oz)

For the Sauce:

- 2 tablespoons olive oil (27.2g; 0.96oz)
- 1 small onion, diced (~100g)
- 3 cloves garlic, minced (~9g)
- 1 can (15 ounces) white beans, drained and rinsed (425g)
- 1/2 cup sun-dried tomatoes, thinly sliced (oil-packed, drained) (~85g)

- 1/2 cup vegetable broth (120g; 4.2oz)
- 2 cups fresh spinach, chopped (60g)
- 1/4 cup fresh basil, chopped (5g)
- 1 tablespoon lemon juice (15g; 0.5oz)
- Salt and pepper to taste (~1.5g salt; ~0.6g pepper)

For Garnish:

- Fresh basil leaves (as needed)
- Grated Parmesan cheese (optional, or use a dairy-free alternative) (~25g)
- Lemon zest (as needed)

Directions:

Prepare the Gnocchi:

1. Bring a large pot of salted water to a boil.
2. Add the gnocchi and cook according to package instructions until they float to the top, about 2-3 minutes.
3. Drain the gnocchi and set aside.

Prepare the Sauce:

4. In a large skillet, heat 2 tablespoons of olive oil over medium heat.
5. Add the diced onion and sauté until translucent, about 5 minutes.
6. Add the minced garlic and cook for another minute until fragrant.
7. Stir in the white beans and sliced sun-dried tomatoes, and cook for 2-3 minutes until heated through.
8. Add the vegetable broth and bring the mixture to a simmer. Cook for 5 minutes, allowing the flavors to meld together.

Combine and Serve:

9. Add the cooked gnocchi to the skillet and toss to coat with the sauce.
10. Stir in the chopped spinach and fresh basil, cooking for another 2 minutes until the spinach is wilted.
11. Stir in the lemon juice and season with salt and pepper to taste.

Serve:

12. Divide the white bean and sun-dried tomato gnocchi among four bowls.
13. Garnish with fresh basil leaves, grated Parmesan cheese (if using), and lemon zest.

CHAPTER 7:
SNACKS!

BAKED VEGGIE TURMERIC BITES

Time: 50 minutes
Serving size: 4

You're going to thank me later. These are little anti-inflammatory mouth bombs. Simple to make and a great snack!

Nutritional Information (Approximate per 1 serving):

Calories: 180 kcal | Protein: 5g | Carbohydrates: 22g | Dietary Fiber: 5g |
Sugars: 4g | Fat: 8g | Saturated Fat: 1g | Sodium: 400mg

Beneficial Nutrients & Anti-Inflammatories:

Turmeric: Curcumin | Carrots: Beta-carotene, vitamin A | Zucchini: Vitamin C, manganese, antioxidants | Sweet Potato: Beta-carotene, vitamins A and C | Garlic: Allicin, antioxidants | Olive Oil: Monounsaturated fats, antioxidants | Chickpea Flour: Fiber, protein, antioxidants

Ingredients:

For the Veggie Bites:

- 1 cup grated carrot (~110g)
- 1 cup grated zucchini (excess moisture squeezed out) (~150g)
- 1 cup grated sweet potato (~200g)
- 1/2 cup chickpea flour (60g)
- 2 tablespoons olive oil (27.2g; 0.96oz)
- 2 cloves garlic, minced (~6g)
- 1 teaspoon ground turmeric (3g)
- 1 teaspoon ground cumin (3g)

- 1/2 teaspoon ground coriander (1g)
- 1/2 teaspoon salt (3g)
- 1/4 teaspoon ground black pepper (0.6g)
- 1/4 teaspoon cayenne pepper (optional for heat) (0.5g)
- 1/4 cup fresh parsley, chopped (4g)

For Garnish:

- Fresh parsley, chopped (as needed)
- Lemon wedges (for serving) (~70g)

Directions:

Prepare the Veggie Mixture:

1. Preheat your oven to 400°F (200°C).
2. In a large bowl, combine the grated carrot, grated zucchini, and grated sweet potato.
3. Add the chickpea flour, minced garlic, olive oil, ground turmeric, ground cumin, ground coriander, salt, ground black pepper, cayenne pepper (if using), and chopped fresh parsley.
4. Mix well until all the ingredients are evenly incorporated and the mixture holds together when pressed.

Shape and Bake the Veggie Bites:

5. Line a baking sheet with parchment paper or lightly grease it.
6. Using your hands, form the veggie mixture into small bite-sized patties or balls, about 1 1/2 inches in diameter.
7. Place the veggie bites on the prepared baking sheet, spacing them evenly.
8. Bake in the preheated oven for 25-30 minutes, or until golden brown and crispy, flipping them halfway through the baking time.

Serve:

9. Remove the veggie bites from the oven and let them cool slightly.
10. Transfer to a serving platter and garnish with additional chopped fresh parsley and lemon wedges.

BLUEBERRY & ALMOND BUTTER SMOOTHIE

Time: 10 minutes
Serving size: 4 smoothies

Nothing better than a smoothie, right? They're the ultimate lazy person's food. Just put everything in a blender and hit the button. Done. You have blueberries, chia seeds, a little spinach, banana, and delicious almond butter in this one. Gotta have it!

Nutritional Information (Approximate per 1 serving):

Calories: 250 kcal | Protein: 8g | Carbohydrates: 30g | Dietary Fiber: 6g |
Sugars: 18g | Fat: 12g | Saturated Fat: 1g | Sodium: 100mg

Beneficial Nutrients & Anti-Inflammatories:

Blueberries: Anthocyanins, vitamin C, antioxidants | Almond Butter: Monounsaturated fats, vitamin E, antioxidants | Spinach: Vitamins A, C, K, antioxidants | Chia Seeds: Omega-3 fatty acids, fiber, antioxidants | Banana: Potassium, vitamin B6, vitamin C

Ingredients:

- 1 cup frozen blueberries (150g)
- 1 ripe banana (~120g)
- 2 tablespoons almond butter (32g)
- 1 cup unsweetened almond milk (or any non-dairy milk of your choice) (240g; 8.5oz)
- 1/2 cup fresh spinach leaves (15g)
- 1 tablespoon chia seeds (12g)
- 1 tablespoon maple syrup (optional, for added sweetness) (20g; 0.7oz)

- 1/2 teaspoon vanilla extract (optional) (2g)

For Garnish:
- Fresh blueberries (as needed)
- Sliced almonds (as needed)
- A sprinkle of chia seeds (as needed)

Directions:

Prepare the Smoothie:

1. In a blender, combine the frozen blueberries, banana, almond butter, almond milk, spinach leaves, chia seeds, maple syrup or honey (if using), and vanilla extract (if using).
2. Blend on high speed until smooth and creamy. If the smoothie is too thick, add a little more almond milk until you reach your desired consistency.

Serve:

3. Pour the smoothie into glasses.
4. Garnish with fresh blueberries, sliced almonds, and a sprinkle of chia seeds.
5. Serve immediately.

CHERRY-COCOA-PISTACHIO ENERGY BALLS

Time: 15 minutes
Serving size: 4

Cherry and cocoa go well together, and both are anti-inflammatory.

Nutritional Information (Approximate per 1 serving):

Calories: 250 kcal | Protein: 6g | Carbohydrates: 30g | Dietary Fiber: 6g | Sugars: 8g | Fat: 12g | Saturated Fat: 2g | Sodium: 50mg

Beneficial Nutrients & Anti-Inflammatories:

Cherries: Anthocyanins, vitamin C, antioxidants | Cocoa: Flavonoids, antioxidants | Pistachios: Healthy fats, vitamin E, antioxidants | Almonds: Monounsaturated fats, vitamin E, antioxidants | Chia Seeds: Omega-3 fatty acids, fiber, antioxidants | Honey: Antioxidants (in moderation)

Ingredients:

- 1 cup dried cherries (160g)
- 1/2 cup unsalted pistachios, shelled (65g)
- 1/2 cup almonds (75g)
- 2 tablespoons cocoa powder (12g)
- 2 tablespoons chia seeds (24g)
- 2 tablespoons honey or maple syrup (40g)
- 1 tablespoon coconut oil, melted (13.6g; 0.48oz)
- 1 teaspoon vanilla extract (4g)
- Pinch of salt (~0.3g)

Directions:

Prepare the Mixture:

1. In a food processor, combine the dried cherries, pistachios, almonds, cocoa powder, chia seeds, honey or maple syrup, melted coconut oil, vanilla extract, and a pinch of salt.

2. Process until the mixture is well combined and sticks together when pressed. If the mixture is too dry, add a little more honey or a small amount of water, one teaspoon at a time, until the desired consistency is reached.

Form the Energy Balls:

3. Scoop out about 1 tablespoon of the mixture and roll it between your hands to form a ball.

4. Repeat with the remaining mixture until all the energy balls are formed.

Optional: Coat the Energy Balls

5. Roll the energy balls in additional cocoa powder or finely chopped pistachios for extra flavor and a decorative touch.

Serve:

6. Arrange the Cherry-Cocoa-Pistachio Energy Balls on a serving plate or store them in an airtight container in the refrigerator.

CHOCOLATE, PEANUT BUTTER & OATS ENERGY BARS

Time: 45 minutes
Serving size: 8

A classic combo. This one includes chia seeds and dark chocolate for the anti-inflammatories.

Nutritional Information (Approximate per 1 serving):

Calories: 250 kcal | Protein: 8g | Carbohydrates: 30g | Dietary Fiber: 5g |
Sugars: 12g | Fat: 12g | Saturated Fat: 3g | Sodium: 100mg

Beneficial Nutrients & Anti-Inflammatories:

Oats: Fiber, antioxidants | Dark Chocolate: Flavonoids, antioxidants | Peanut Butter: Monounsaturated fats, vitamin E, antioxidants | Chia Seeds: Omega-3 fatty acids, fiber, antioxidants | Honey: Antioxidants (in moderation)

Ingredients:

- 1 1/2 cups rolled oats (use Bob's Red Mill) (135g)
- 1/2 cup peanut butter (natural, no added sugar or salt) (128g)
- 1/4 cup honey or maple syrup (for vegan option) (60g)
- 1/4 cup dark chocolate chips (at least 70% cocoa) (45g)
- 1/4 cup chia seeds (30g)
- 1/4 cup ground flaxseeds (30g)

- 1/4 cup unsweetened shredded coconut (20g)
- 1/4 cup almond milk (or any non-dairy milk of your choice) (60g)
- 1 teaspoon vanilla extract (4g)
- Pinch of salt (~0.3g)

For Topping:
- 2 tablespoons dark chocolate chips (15g)
- 1 tablespoon peanut butter (16g)

Directions:

Prepare the Mixture:

1. In a large bowl, combine the rolled oats, peanut butter, honey or maple syrup, dark chocolate chips, chia seeds, ground flaxseeds, unsweetened shredded coconut, almond milk, vanilla extract, and a pinch of salt.
2. Mix well until all the ingredients are evenly incorporated and the mixture holds together when pressed.

Form the Bars:

3. Line an 8x8 inch baking dish with parchment paper, leaving some overhang on the sides for easy removal.
4. Press the mixture firmly and evenly into the prepared baking dish.

Prepare the Topping:

5. In a microwave-safe bowl, combine the 2 tablespoons of dark chocolate chips and 1 tablespoon of peanut butter.
6. Microwave in 15-second intervals, stirring in between, until the chocolate and peanut butter are melted and smooth.
7. Drizzle the melted chocolate and peanut butter over the pressed mixture in the baking dish.

Chill the Bars:

8. Place the baking dish in the refrigerator and chill for at least 30 minutes, or until the bars are firm and set.

Serve:

9. Once set, remove the mixture from the baking dish using the parchment paper overhang.
10. Cut into 8 equal bars.

CHICKPEA PUFFS

Time: 40 minutes
Serving size: 4

I often double this recipe and keep these stored in a container for the week. They help to keep me away from my salty snack cravings (potato chips) and are really delicious.

Nutritional Information (per serving, assuming 4 servings):

Calories: 150 kcal | Protein: 6g | Carbohydrates: 22g | Dietary Fiber: 6g |
Sugars: 2g | Fat: 4g | Saturated Fat: 0.5g | Sodium: 200mg

Beneficial Nutrients & Anti-Inflammatories:

Chickpeas: Fiber, protein, antioxidants | Olive Oil: Monounsaturated fats, antioxidants | Turmeric: Curcumin | Cumin: Anti-inflammatory properties | Paprika: Capsaicin, antioxidants

Ingredients:

- 1 can (15 ounces) chickpeas, drained and rinsed (425g)
- 1 tablespoon olive oil (13.6g; 0.48oz)
- 1/2 teaspoon ground turmeric (1.5g)
- 1/2 teaspoon ground cumin (1.5g)

- 1/2 teaspoon smoked paprika (1.2g)
- 1/4 teaspoon garlic powder (0.8g)
- 1/4 teaspoon onion powder (0.7g)
- 1/4 teaspoon salt (1.5g)
- 1/4 teaspoon ground black pepper (0.6g)

Directions:

Prepare the Chickpeas:

1. Preheat your oven to 400°F (200°C).
2. Drain and rinse the chickpeas thoroughly. Pat them dry with a paper towel to remove any excess moisture.

Season the Chickpeas:

3. In a large bowl, toss the chickpeas with olive oil, ground turmeric, ground cumin, smoked paprika, garlic powder, onion powder, salt, and ground black pepper until evenly coated.

Bake the Chickpeas:

4. Spread the seasoned chickpeas in a single layer on a baking sheet lined with parchment paper.
5. Bake in the preheated oven for 25-30 minutes, or until the chickpeas are golden brown and crispy, stirring halfway through the cooking time to ensure even baking.

Serve:

6. Remove the chickpeas from the oven and let them cool slightly.
7. Serve the chickpea puffs immediately, or store them in an airtight container for up to one week.

FROZEN STRAWBERRY-DARK CHOCOLATE YOGURT BARS

Time: 4 hours 15 minutes
Serving size: 8

Don't cheat and buy the milk-based chocolate chips, make sure you get the dairy free dark chocolate chips. I'm watching you!

Nutritional Information (Approximate per 1 serving):

Calories: 150 kcal | Protein: 3g | Carbohydrates: 20g | Dietary Fiber: 3g |
Sugars: 15g | Fat: 7g | Saturated Fat: 4g | Sodium: 50mg

Beneficial Nutrients & Anti-Inflammatories:

Strawberries: Vitamin C, antioxidants | Dark Chocolate: Flavonoids, antioxidants | Almonds: Monounsaturated fats,
vitamin E, antioxidants | Coconut Yogurt: Healthy fats, probiotics (if included)

Ingredients:

For the Yogurt Bars:

- 2 cups non-dairy yogurt (coconut or almond yogurt) (480g)
- 1 cup fresh strawberries, sliced (~150g)
- 1/4 cup maple syrup or agave syrup (60g)
- 1 teaspoon vanilla extract (4g)

For the Chocolate Swirl:

- 1/2 cup dark chocolate chips (dairy-free) (90g)
- 1 tablespoon coconut oil (13.6g; 0.48oz)

For Garnish:

- Fresh strawberries, sliced (as needed)
- Chopped almonds or other nuts (optional) (as needed)

Directions:

Prepare the Yogurt Mixture:

1. In a medium bowl, combine the non-dairy yogurt, sliced strawberries, maple syrup or agave syrup, and vanilla extract.
2. Mix until well combined.

Prepare the Chocolate Swirl:

3. In a microwave-safe bowl, combine the dark chocolate chips and coconut oil.
4. Microwave in 15-second intervals, stirring in between, until the chocolate and coconut oil are melted and smooth.

Assemble the Bars:

5. Line an 8x8 inch baking dish with parchment paper, leaving some overhang on the sides for easy removal.
6. Pour the yogurt mixture into the prepared baking dish and spread it out evenly.
7. Drizzle the melted chocolate mixture over the top of the yogurt mixture.
8. Use a knife or toothpick to swirl the chocolate into the yogurt.

Freeze the Bars:

9. Place the baking dish in the freezer and freeze for at least 4 hours, or until the bars are firm and set.

Serve:

10. Once the bars are frozen, remove them from the freezer and let them sit at room temperature for a few minutes to soften slightly.
11. Use the parchment paper overhang to lift the frozen yogurt slab out of the baking dish.
12. Cut into 8 equal bars.
13. Devour.

HIBISCUS GINGER GUMMIES

Time: 2 hours 15 minutes
Serving size: 4

Great for a quick snack and easy to take with you on the go! Hibiscus has a complex flavor that's sweet, tart, and refreshing, with notes of cranberry, pomegranate, or lemon. It also has earthy undertones and can be slightly acidic.

Nutritional Information (Approximate per 1 serving):

Calories: 50 kcal | Protein: 5g | Carbohydrates: 8g | Dietary Fiber: 0g | Sugars: 6g | Fat: 0g | Saturated Fat: 0g | Sodium: 10mg

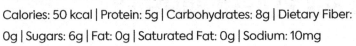

Beneficial Nutrients & Anti-Inflammatories:

Hibiscus: Antioxidants, vitamin C | Ginger: Gingerol, other antioxidants | Honey: Antioxidants (in moderation) | Gelatin: Protein, gut health benefits

Ingredients:

- 1 cup water (240g)
- 2 tablespoons dried hibiscus flowers, or hibiscus tea (6g)
- 1 tablespoon fresh ginger, grated (6g)
- 2-3 tablespoons maple syrup (adjust to taste) (30-45g)
- 2 tablespoons lemon juice (30g; 1.02oz)
- 3 tablespoons gelatin powder (use agar-agar for vegan option) (24g)

Directions:

Prepare the Hibiscus Ginger Tea:

1. In a small saucepan, bring 1 cup of water to a boil.
2. Remove from heat and add the dried hibiscus flowers (or tea) and grated ginger.
3. Cover and let steep for 10 minutes.

Strain the Tea:

4. Strain the hibiscus ginger tea into a medium bowl to remove the flowers and ginger pieces.
5. Stir in the maple syrup and lemon juice until fully dissolved. Adjust the sweetness to taste.

Prepare the Gelatin Mixture:

6. Sprinkle the gelatin powder over the hibiscus ginger tea and whisk until fully dissolved. If using agar-agar, follow the package instructions for dissolving it.

Heat the Mixture:

7. Return the mixture to the saucepan and gently heat over low heat, stirring constantly, until the gelatin is fully dissolved and the mixture is smooth (do not boil).

Pour into Molds:

8. Pour the mixture into silicone molds or a shallow baking dish.
9. Refrigerate for at least 2 hours, or until the gummies are firm.

Serve:

10. Once set, remove the gummies from the molds or cut them into bite-sized pieces if using a baking dish.
11. Store the gummies in an airtight container in the refrigerator for up to one week.

TURMERIC & BLACK PEPPER GUMMIES

Time: 2 hours 15 minutes
Serving size: 4

You're going to love these. Easy to make and carry with you. These are little anti-inflammatory powerhouses!

Nutritional Information (Approximate per 1 serving):

Calories: 40 kcal | Protein: 5g | Carbohydrates: 6g | Dietary Fiber: 0g | Sugars: 4g | Fat: 0g | Saturated Fat: 0g | Sodium: 10mg

Beneficial Nutrients & Anti-Inflammatories:

Turmeric: Curcumin | Black Pepper: Piperine | Honey: Antioxidants (in moderation) | Gelatin: Protein, gut health benefits

Ingredients:

- 1 cup water or coconut water (240g)
- 1 tablespoon ground turmeric (9g)
- 1/2 teaspoon ground black pepper (1.2g)
- 2-3 tablespoons maple syrup (adjust to taste) (30-45g)

- 3 tablespoons gelatin powder (use agar-agar for vegan option) (24g)
- 1 tablespoon lemon juice (optional) (15g; 0.5oz)

Directions:

Prepare the Turmeric Mixture:

1. In a small saucepan, bring 1 cup of water or coconut water to a boil.
2. Remove from heat and stir in the ground turmeric, ground black pepper, honey or maple syrup, and lemon juice (if using). Mix until fully dissolved. Adjust sweetness to taste.

Prepare the Gelatin Mixture:

3. Sprinkle the gelatin powder over the turmeric mixture and whisk until fully dissolved. If using agar-agar, follow the package instructions for dissolving it.

Heat the Mixture:

4. Return the mixture to the saucepan and gently heat over low heat, stirring constantly, until the gelatin is fully dissolved and the mixture is smooth (do not boil).

Pour into Molds:

5. Pour the mixture into silicone molds or a shallow baking dish.
6. Refrigerate for at least 2 hours, or until the gummies are firm.

Serve:

7. Once set, remove the gummies from the molds or cut them into bite-sized pieces if using a baking dish.
8. Store the gummies in an airtight container in the refrigerator for up to one week.

LEMON-BLUEBERRY BARS

Time: 2 hours 55 minutes
Serving size: 16

Why did the lemon refuse to play cards with the blueberries? Because it was afraid of getting squeezed! *Ha!* Ahem. This snack is made with almond and coconut flours, and plenty of lemon and blueberry! What's not to love?

Nutritional Information (Approximate per 1 serving):

Calories: 150 kcal | Protein: 2g | Carbohydrates: 22g | Dietary Fiber: 2g | Sugars: 15g | Fat: 6g | Saturated Fat: 2g | Sodium: 100mg

Beneficial Nutrients & Anti-Inflammatories:

Blueberries: Anthocyanins, vitamin C, antioxidants | Lemon: Vitamin C, antioxidants | Almond Flour: Vitamin E, healthy fats, antioxidants

Ingredients:

For the Crust:

- 1 cup almond flour (96g)
- 1/2 cup oat flour (use gluten-free if needed) (60g)
- 1/4 cup coconut oil, melted (54.4g; 1.92oz)
- 1/4 cup maple syrup (60g)
- 1/2 teaspoon vanilla extract (2g)
- Pinch of salt (~0.3g)

For the Filling:

- 2 cups fresh or frozen blueberries (300g)
- 1/4 cup lemon juice (60g; 2.1oz)
- 1 tablespoon lemon zest (6g)

- 1/4 cup maple syrup (60g)
- 3 large eggs (150g)
- 1/4 cup coconut flour (30g)
- 1/2 teaspoon vanilla extract (2g)

For Garnish:

- Powdered sugar (optional, as needed)
- Fresh blueberries (as needed)
- Lemon zest (as needed)

Directions:

Prepare the Crust:

1. Preheat your oven to 350°F (175°C).
2. Line an 8x8 inch baking dish with parchment paper, leaving some overhang on the sides for easy removal.
3. In a medium bowl, combine the almond flour, oat flour, melted coconut oil, maple syrup or honey, vanilla extract, and a pinch of salt. Mix until well combined.
4. Press the mixture firmly and evenly into the prepared baking dish.
5. Bake in the preheated oven for 10-12 minutes, or until the crust is lightly golden. Remove from the oven and set aside.

Prepare the Filling:

6. In a blender or food processor, combine the blueberries, lemon juice, lemon zest, maple syrup or honey, eggs, coconut flour, and vanilla extract. Blend until smooth.
7. Pour the blueberry mixture over the pre-baked crust, spreading it out evenly.

Bake the Bars:

8. Bake in the preheated oven for 20-25 minutes, or until the filling is set and the edges are golden.
9. Remove from the oven and let the bars cool completely in the baking dish.

Chill the Bars:

10. Once cooled, refrigerate the bars for at least 2 hours to allow them to set fully.

Serve:

11. Once set, use the parchment paper overhang to lift the bars out of the baking dish.
12. Cut into 16 equal squares.

MANGO, DATE & CHIA ENERGY BITES

Time: 1 hour 15 minutes
Serving size: 16

I eat way too many of these. I probably shouldn't. Or should I? The angel and devil on my shoulders are always hard at work.

Nutritional Information (Approximate per 1 serving):

Calories: 120 kcal | Protein: 2g | Carbohydrates: 20g | Dietary Fiber: 3g |
Sugars: 15g | Fat: 4g | Saturated Fat: 1g | Sodium: 20mg

Beneficial Nutrients & Anti-Inflammatories:

Mango: Vitamin C, beta-carotene, antioxidants | Dates: Fiber, antioxidants | Chia Seeds: Omega-3 fatty acids, fiber, antioxidants | Almonds: Monounsaturated fats, vitamin E, antioxidants

....

Ingredients:

- 1 cup dried mango, chopped (160g)
- 1 cup dates, pitted and chopped (160g)
- 1/2 cup almonds (75g)
- 2 tablespoons chia seeds (24g)

- 1 tablespoon coconut oil (13.6g; 0.48oz)
- 1 teaspoon vanilla extract (4g)
- Pinch of salt (~0.3g)

....

Directions:

Prepare the Mixture:

1. In a food processor, combine the dried mango, dates, almonds, chia seeds, coconut oil, vanilla extract, and a pinch of salt.
2. Process until the mixture is well combined and sticky. If the mixture is too dry, add a small amount of water, one teaspoon at a time, until it reaches the desired consistency.

Form the Energy Bites:

3. Using your hands, scoop out about 1 tablespoon of the mixture and roll it into a ball.
4. Repeat with the remaining mixture until all the energy bites are formed.

Chill the Bites:

5. Place the energy bites on a baking sheet lined with parchment paper.
6. Refrigerate for at least 1 hour to allow the bites to firm up.

Serve:

7. Once chilled, transfer the energy bites to an airtight container.
8. Store in the refrigerator for up to one week.

PEANUT BUTTER BLUEBERRY ENERGY BALLS

Time: 1 hour 15 minutes
Serving size: 16

I mean...what's not to like? Like any "energy ball" recipe, just make sure you eat these in moderation. Which I tend *not* to do.

Nutritional Information (Approximate per 1 serving):

Calories: 130 kcal | Protein: 4g | Carbohydrates: 14g | Dietary Fiber: 3g | Sugars: 8g | Fat: 7g | Saturated Fat: 1g | Sodium: 50mg

Beneficial Nutrients & Anti-Inflammatories:

Blueberries: Anthocyanins, vitamin C, antioxidants | Peanut Butter: Monounsaturated fats, vitamin E, antioxidants | Oats: Fiber, antioxidants | Chia Seeds: Omega-3 fatty acids, fiber, antioxidants | Flaxseeds: Omega-3 fatty acids, fiber, antioxidants

Ingredients:

- 1 cup rolled oats (Bob's Red Mill) (90g)
- 1/2 cup natural peanut butter (no added sugar or salt) (128g)
- 1/4 cup maple syrup (60g)
- 1/2 cup dried blueberries (80g)
- 2 tablespoons chia seeds (24g)
- 2 tablespoons ground flaxseeds (14g)
- 1 teaspoon vanilla extract (4g)
- Pinch of salt (~0.3g)

Directions:

Prepare the Mixture:

1. In a large bowl, combine the rolled oats, peanut butter, honey or maple syrup, dried blueberries, chia seeds, ground flaxseeds, vanilla extract, and a pinch of salt.
2. Mix well until all the ingredients are evenly incorporated and the mixture holds together when pressed. If the mixture is too dry, add a small amount of water, one teaspoon at a time, until it reaches the desired consistency.

Form the Energy Balls:

3. Using your hands, scoop out about 1 tablespoon of the mixture and roll it into a ball.
4. Repeat with the remaining mixture until all the energy balls are formed.

Chill the Balls:

5. Place the energy balls on a baking sheet lined with parchment paper.
6. Refrigerate for at least 1 hour to allow the balls to firm up.

Serve:

7. Once chilled, transfer the energy balls to an airtight container.
8. Store in the refrigerator for up to one week.

PINEAPPLE-GRAPEFRUIT DETOX SMOOTHIE

Time: 10 minutes
Serving size: 2

This is really delicious and refreshing. Perfect for a summer day! You can easily adjust the sugar by limiting or eliminating the maple syrup altogether.

Nutritional Information (Approximate per 1 serving):

Calories: 150 kcal | Protein: 2g | Carbohydrates: 35g | Dietary Fiber: 5g | Sugars: 16g | Fat: 1g | Saturated Fat: 0g | Sodium: 10mg

Beneficial Nutrients & Anti-Inflammatories:

Pineapple: Bromelain, vitamin C, antioxidants | Grapefruit: Vitamin C, antioxidants | Ginger: Gingerol, other antioxidants | Turmeric: Curcumin | Spinach: Vitamins A, C, K, antioxidants | Chia Seeds: Omega-3 fatty acids, fiber, antioxidants

Ingredients:

- 1 cup fresh pineapple chunks (~165g)
- 1 grapefruit, peeled and segmented (~230g)
- 1/2 cup fresh spinach leaves (15g)
- 1/2 inch fresh ginger root, peeled and grated (~2g)
- 1/2 teaspoon ground turmeric (1.5g)
- 1 tablespoon chia seeds (12g)

- 1 cup coconut water (240g; 8.5oz)
- 1 tablespoon lemon juice (15g; 0.5oz)
- 1 teaspoon maple syrup (optional, adjust to taste) (5g)
- Ice cubes (optional, for a colder smoothie) (as needed)

Directions:

Prepare the Smoothie:

1. In a blender, combine the fresh pineapple chunks, grapefruit segments, spinach leaves, grated ginger, ground turmeric, chia seeds, coconut water, lemon juice, and honey or maple syrup (if using).

2. Blend on high speed until smooth and creamy. If you prefer a colder smoothie, add a few ice cubes and blend again until smooth.

Serve:

3. Pour the smoothie into two glasses.

4. Garnish with a sprinkle of chia seeds or a slice of pineapple or grapefruit if desired.

SAVORY DATE & PISTACHIO BITES

Time: 1 hour 15 minutes
Serving size: 16

Savory and sweet! Loaded with anti-inflammatories! Eat eat eat!

Nutritional Information (Approximate per 1 serving):

Calories: 120 kcal | Protein: 2g | Carbohydrates: 18g | Dietary Fiber: 3g |
Sugars: 14g | Fat: 5g | Saturated Fat: 0.5g | Sodium: 50mg

Beneficial Nutrients & Anti-Inflammatories:

Dates: Fiber, antioxidants | Pistachios: Healthy fats, vitamin E, antioxidants | Olive Oil: Monounsaturated fats, antioxidants | Turmeric: Curcumin | Garlic: Allicin, antioxidants

....

Ingredients:

- 1 cup pitted dates (160g)
- 1/2 cup shelled pistachios (65g)
- 1/4 cup almond flour (24g)
- 1 tablespoon olive oil (13.6g; 0.48oz)
- 1 teaspoon ground turmeric (3g)
- 1 teaspoon ground cumin (3g)

- 1/2 teaspoon garlic powder (1.6g)
- 1/2 teaspoon smoked paprika (1.2g)
- 1/2 teaspoon sea salt (3g)
- 1 tablespoon fresh parsley, finely chopped (optional for garnish) (4g)

....

Directions:

Prepare the Mixture:

1. In a food processor, combine the pitted dates and shelled pistachios. Process until the mixture is finely chopped and starts to come together.
2. Add the almond flour, olive oil, ground turmeric, ground cumin, garlic powder, smoked paprika, and sea salt. Process again until all ingredients are well combined and the mixture forms a sticky dough.

Form the Bites:

3. Using your hands, scoop out about 1 tablespoon of the mixture and roll it into a ball.
4. Repeat with the remaining mixture until all the bites are formed.

Chill the Bites:

5. Place the date and pistachio bites on a baking sheet lined with parchment paper.
6. Refrigerate for at least 1 hour to allow the bites to firm up.

Serve:

7. Once chilled, transfer the bites to an airtight container.
8. Store in the refrigerator for up to one week.

SUPER-SEED SNACK BARS

Time: 1 hour 15 minutes
Serving size: 16

Lots and lots of beneficial seeds, combined with coconut, cranberries, vanilla, cinnamon, and a touch of healthy sweetner. Really good.

Nutritional Information (Approximate per 1 serving):

Calories: 180 kcal | Protein: 5g | Carbohydrates: 15g | Dietary Fiber: 4g |
Sugars: 8g | Fat: 10g | Saturated Fat: 2g | Sodium: 50mg

Beneficial Nutrients & Anti-Inflammatories:

Chia Seeds: Omega-3 fatty acids, fiber, antioxidants | Flaxseeds: Omega-3 fatty acids, fiber, antioxidants | Pumpkin Seeds: Zinc, magnesium, antioxidants | Sunflower Seeds: Vitamin E, healthy fats, antioxidants | Coconut Oil: Lauric acid, antioxidants | Honey: Antioxidants (in moderation)

Ingredients:

- 1 cup rolled oats (Bob's Red Mill) (90g)
- 1/2 cup chia seeds (60g)
- 1/2 cup ground flaxseeds (30g)
- 1/2 cup pumpkin seeds (60g)
- 1/2 cup sunflower seeds (70g)
- 1/4 cup dried cranberries (or other dried fruit) (40g)
- 1/4 cup shredded coconut (unsweetened) (20g)
- 1/2 cup maple syrup (120g)
- 1/4 cup coconut oil, melted (54.4g; 1.92oz)
- 1 teaspoon vanilla extract (4g)
- 1/2 teaspoon ground cinnamon (1.3g)
- Pinch of salt (~0.3g)

Directions:

Prepare the Mixture:
1. In a large mixing bowl, combine the rolled oats, chia seeds, ground flaxseeds, pumpkin seeds, sunflower seeds, dried cranberries, and shredded coconut. Mix well.

Combine Wet Ingredients:
2. In a small saucepan, combine the honey or maple syrup, melted coconut oil, vanilla extract, ground cinnamon, and a pinch of salt.
3. Heat over low heat, stirring occasionally, until the mixture is well combined and smooth.

Mix and Combine:
4. Pour the warm wet ingredients over the dry mixture in the large bowl.
5. Stir well until all the dry ingredients are thoroughly coated with the wet mixture.

Form the Bars:
6. Line an 8x8 inch baking dish with parchment paper, leaving some overhang on the sides for easy removal.
7. Transfer the mixture to the prepared baking dish and press it down firmly and evenly.

Chill the Bars:
8. Place the baking dish in the refrigerator and chill for at least 1 hour, or until the mixture is -firm and set.

Serve:
9. Once set, use the parchment paper overhang to lift the mixture out of the baking dish.
10. Cut into 16 equal bars.

SWEET POTATO & KALE BALLS

Time: 45 minutes
Serving size: 16

A surprising and delightful combination. Low calorie and packed full of anti-inflammatory goodness!

Nutritional Information (Approximate per 1 serving):

Calories: 80 kcal | Protein: 2g | Carbohydrates: 14g | Dietary Fiber: 3g | Sugars: 3g | Fat: 2g | Saturated Fat: 0.5g | Sodium: 150mg

Beneficial Nutrients & Anti-Inflammatories:

Sweet Potatoes: Beta-carotene, vitamins A and C | Kale: Vitamins A, C, K, antioxidants | Garlic: Allicin, antioxidants | Olive Oil: Monounsaturated fats, antioxidants | Turmeric: Curcumin

Ingredients:

- 2 medium sweet potatoes, peeled and cubed (~400g)
- 2 cups kale, finely chopped (stems removed) (60g)
- 2 cloves garlic, minced (~6g)
- 2 tablespoons olive oil (27.2g; 0.96oz)
- 1/2 teaspoon ground turmeric (1.5g)
- 1/2 teaspoon ground cumin (1.5g)
- 1/2 teaspoon smoked paprika (1.2g)
- 1/4 teaspoon ground black pepper (0.6g)

- 1/2 teaspoon salt (3g)
- 1/4 cup almond flour (or breadcrumbs) (24g)
- 1/4 cup grated Parmesan cheese (optional, use dairy-free cheese for vegan option) (25g)

For Garnish:

- Fresh parsley, chopped (as needed)
- Lemon wedges (for serving) (~70g)

Directions:

Prepare the Sweet Potatoes:

1. Preheat your oven to 400°F (200°C).
2. Place the cubed sweet potatoes in a pot of boiling water. Cook for about 10-12 minutes, or until tender.
3. Drain the sweet potatoes and transfer them to a large mixing bowl. Mash until smooth.

Prepare the Kale:

4. In a large skillet, heat 1 tablespoon of olive oil over medium heat.
5. Add the minced garlic and sauté for about 1 minute until fragrant.
6. Add the finely chopped kale and cook for 3-4 minutes until wilted. Remove from heat and set aside.

Combine Ingredients:

7. Add the cooked kale to the mashed sweet potatoes.
8. Stir in the ground turmeric, ground cumin, smoked paprika, ground black pepper, salt, almond flour (or breadcrumbs), and grated Parmesan cheese (if using). Mix well until all ingredients are evenly incorporated.

Form the Balls:

9. Using your hands, scoop out about 1 tablespoon of the mixture and roll it into a ball.
10. Repeat with the remaining mixture until all the balls are formed.

Bake the Balls:

11. Place the sweet potato and kale balls on a baking sheet lined with parchment paper.
12. Brush the balls with the remaining 1 tablespoon of olive oil.
13. Bake in the preheated oven for 15-20 minutes, or until golden brown and slightly crispy.

Serve:

14. Remove the balls from the oven and let them cool slightly.
15. Transfer to a serving plate and garnish with chopped fresh parsley and lemon wedges.

CONCLUSION

Embarking on the journey of an anti-inflammatory diet is a powerful step towards achieving better health and wellness. The anti-inflammatory diet, rich in whole, nutrient-dense foods, has the potential to alleviate chronic inflammation, manage pain, and enhance your quality of life.

As you experiment with these recipes, remember that flexibility is key. Adapt the dishes to your taste preferences, dietary needs, and lifestyle. The goal is to enjoy the process of cooking and eating foods that nourish your body and mind. Take pride in the small victories, whether it's mastering a new recipe, discovering a new favorite ingredient, or simply feeling more energized and healthier.

Thank you for allowing me to be part of your culinary journey. **If you enjoyed this book, I would kindly request that you leave a review on Amazon. It really helps to get it in front of more people!**

Bon appétit!

Allicin: A compound found in garlic known for its anti-inflammatory and antioxidant properties.

Anthocyanins: Pigments found in berries and cherries that have potent antioxidant and anti-inflammatory effects.

Antioxidants: Molecules that prevent oxidation and reduce oxidative stress, thereby combating inflammation and protecting cells from damage.

Apigenin: A flavonoid found in celery that has anti-inflammatory and antioxidant effects.

Beta-carotene: An antioxidant found in carrots and butternut squash that converts to vitamin A in the body and helps reduce inflammation.

Beta-glucans: Polysaccharides found in mushrooms that modulate the immune system and reduce inflammation.

Bromelain: An enzyme found in pineapple that has anti-inflammatory properties and aids digestion.

Calcium: A mineral found in dairy products, leafy greens, and fortified plant-based milks that modulates the immune system and reduces the risk of inflammatory conditions like osteoporosis.

Capsaicin: A compound found in chili peppers that has anti-inflammatory and pain-relieving properties.

Carotenoids: A class of antioxidants found in colorful fruits and vegetables that help reduce inflammation and support immune function.

Catalase: An antioxidant enzyme found in fatty fish that helps protect cells from oxidative damage and reduces inflammation.

Chlorogenic Acid: A polyphenol found in coffee and certain fruits that has antioxidant and anti-inflammatory properties.

Choline: A nutrient found in eggs and other foods that supports brain health and reduces inflammation.

Copper: A mineral found in shellfish, nuts, seeds, and whole grains that supports antioxidant enzyme function, thereby reducing inflammation.

Curcumin: The active ingredient in turmeric with strong anti-inflammatory and antioxidant properties.

Cytokines: Small proteins released by cells that have a specific effect on the interactions and communications between cells, often involved in inflammation.

DHA (Docosahexaenoic Acid): An omega-3 fatty acid found in fatty fish that supports brain health and reduces inflammation.

EPA (Eicosapentaenoic Acid): An omega-3 fatty acid found in fatty fish that reduces inflammation.

Flavonoids: A diverse group of phytonutrients found in many fruits and vegetables with anti-inflammatory, antioxidant, and anti-cancer properties.

Gingerol: The active compound in ginger known for its anti-inflammatory and antioxidant effects.

Glutathione: A powerful antioxidant found in many foods that helps reduce oxidative stress and inflammation.

Hesperidin: A flavonoid found in citrus fruits that has anti-inflammatory and antioxidant properties.

Isoflavones: Compounds found in soy products that have anti-inflammatory properties.

Iron: A mineral found in red meat, poultry, fish, legumes, and leafy greens that is essential for immune function, with deficiency exacerbating inflammation.

Kaempferol: A flavonoid found in many plants that has anti-inflammatory and antioxidant properties.

Lignans: A type of phytoestrogen found in flaxseeds and other seeds that has antioxidant and anti-inflammatory effects.

Lutein: A carotenoid found in leafy greens and other vegetables that supports eye health and reduces inflammation.

Lycopene: An antioxidant found in tomatoes that helps reduce inflammation.

Magnesium: A mineral found in nuts, seeds, leafy greens, and whole grains that reduces CRP levels and regulates cytokines, thus reducing inflammation.

Monounsaturated Fats: Healthy fats found in avocados and olive oil that reduce inflammation and improve heart health.

Myricetin: A flavonoid found in berries and other fruits that has antioxidant and anti-inflammatory properties.

Oleic Acid: A monounsaturated fat found in olive oil and avocados that reduces inflammation.

Oleocanthal: A phenolic compound in olive oil with anti-inflammatory properties similar to ibuprofen.

Omega-3 Fatty Acids: Essential fats with powerful anti-inflammatory effects, found in high amounts in fatty fish.

Phytonutrients: Natural compounds found in plants that have health-promoting properties, including anti-inflammatory effects.

Polyphenols: Micronutrients with antioxidant activity found in a variety of plant foods that help reduce inflammation.

Piperine: An alkaloid found in black pepper that enhances the absorption of curcumin and other nutrients.

Potassium: A mineral found in bananas, avocados, leafy greens, and potatoes that helps regulate blood pressure and reduces CRP levels.

Quercetin: A flavonoid found in onions and capers with strong antioxidant and anti-inflammatory properties.

Resveratrol: A polyphenol found in grapes with strong antioxidant and anti-inflammatory properties.

Selenium: An antioxidant mineral found in Brazil nuts, seafood, eggs, and whole grains that reduces oxidative stress and lowers CRP levels.

Sulforaphane: A sulfur-containing compound in broccoli that activates antioxidant enzymes and reduces inflammation.

Thymoquinone: A compound found in black cumin seed oil with anti-inflammatory and antioxidant properties.

Turmerones: Compounds found in turmeric that enhance the anti-inflammatory effects of curcumin.

Vitamin A (Retinoids & Carotenoids): Found in liver, carrots, sweet potatoes, and leafy greens. Carotenoids like beta-carotene reduce oxidative stress, while retinoids modulate immune function.

Vitamin B6, B9, & B12: Found in poultry, fish, bananas, chickpeas, leafy greens, legumes, and fortified plant-based foods. These vitamins reduce homocysteine levels and cytokine regulation.

Vitamin C: An antioxidant vitamin found in many fruits and vegetables that helps reduce inflammation and boost the immune system.

Vitamin D: Found in sunlight, fortified foods, fatty fish, and egg yolks. Helps modulate the immune system, reducing pro-inflammatory cytokines.

Vitamin E: A fat-soluble antioxidant found in nuts and seeds that protects cell membranes from oxidative damage and reduces inflammation.

Zeaxanthin: A carotenoid found in leafy greens and other vegetables that supports eye health and reduces inflammation.

Zinc: A mineral found in seafood, meat, seeds, and legumes that modulates the immune response and reduces oxidative stress and inflammatory cytokines.

Ajmera, R., & Sharon, A. (2020, February 20). The 10 best foods to eat if you have arthritis. Healthline. https:/www.healthline.com/health/foods-for-arthritis

Amazing benefits of buying bulk foods. (n.d.). The Source Bulk Foods UK. https:/thesourcebulkfoods.co.uk/blogs/zero-waste/benefits-of-buying-bulk-foods

Ames, H. (2022, February 28). Non-triggering IBS recipes: Breakfast, lunch, dinner, and snacks. Medical News Today. https:/www.medicalnewstoday.com/articles/ibs-recipes#breakfast-recipes

Amidor, T. (2018). Recipe revamp: Make any recipe vegan or vegetarian. Food Network. https:/www.foodnetwork.com/healthyeats/recipes/2015/01/recipe-revamp-make-any-recipe-vegan-or-vegetarian

Anderson-Haynes, S.-E. (n.d.). Creating a grocery list. Eatright.org. https:/www.eatright.org/food/planning/smart-shopping/creating-a-grocery-list

Anti-Inflammatory recipes. (n.d.). EatingWell. https:/www.eatingwell.com/gallery/12952/anti-inflammatory-recipes/

Baltazar, A. (n.d.). Do vegetarian diets reduce arthritis inflammation? Arthritis.org. https:/www.arthritis.org/health-wellness/healthy-living/nutrition/anti-inflammatory/vegetarian-diet-arthritis

Barhum, L. (n.d.). 6 inflammation-fighting vitamins. Verywell Health. https:/www.verywellhealth.com/the-best-vitamin-for-fighting-inflammation-4176859

Barkha. (2021, January 25). Berries benefits, nutritional value, facts & side effects. Wellcurve Blog. https:/www.wellcurve.in/blog/benefits-of-berries-and-nutritional-facts/

Barode, S. (2022, December 8). Basil leaves: Uses, benefits, side effects by Dr. Smita Barode. PharmEasy Blog. https:/pharmeasy.in/blog/ayurveda-uses-benefits-side-effects-of-basil-leaves/

Baskaran-Makanju, S. (2020, April 24). Indian cooking 101: Essential Indian gluten-free ingredients & spices. Urban Farmie. https:/urbanfarmie.com/indian-pantry/

Benefits of buying bulk foods – The source bulk foods. (n.d.). Thesourcebulkfoods.ca. https:/www.thesourcebulkfoods.ca/blog/benefits-of-buying-bulk-foods/

246

Benefits of olive oil for arthritis. (n.d.). Arthritis.org. https:/www.arthritis.org/health-wellness/healthy-living/ nutrition/healthy-eating/olive-oil-benefits-arthritis

Benisek, A. (2008, July 30). Best and worst foods for diabetes. WebMD. https:/www.webmd.com/diabetes/ diabetic-food-list-best-worst-foods

Best fish for arthritis. (n.d.). Arthritis.org. https:/www.arthritis.org/health-wellness/healthy-living/nutrition/ healthy-eating/best-fish-for-arthritis

Best nuts and seeds for arthritis. (n.d.). Arthritis.org. https:/www.arthritis.org/health-wellness/healthy-living/ nutrition/healthy-eating/best-nuts-and-seeds-for-arthritis

Blessed Beyond Crazy. (2015, May 16). How to make almost any recipe gluten-free. Blessed Beyond Crazy. https:/blessedbeyondcrazy.com/how-to-make-almost-any-recipe-gluten-free/

Bolen, B. (n.d.-a). How to eat better for treating your IBS symptoms. Verywell Health. https:/www. verywellhealth.com/the-ten-best-foods-for-ibs-1945014

Bolen, B. (n.d.-b). How you can keep a food diary to help identify food sensitivities. Verywell Health. https:/www.verywellhealth.com/how-to-keep-a-food-diary-1945006#:~:text=Look%20for%20 Patterns%3A%20At%20the

Bolen, B. (n.d.-c). Will going gluten-free help your IBS? Verywell Health. https:/www.verywellhealth.com/ibs-and-gluten-sensitivity-1944840#:~:text=The%20gluten%2Dfree%20diet%20often

Bucci, K. (2023, March 31). Easy nut and fruit trail mix. My Table of Three. https:/www.mytableofthree.com/ easy-nut-and-fruit-trail-mix/

Butter, J. (2010, March). Modify a recipe for healthy results. Rutgers University. https:/njaes.rutgers.edu/sshw/ message/message.php?m=152&p=Health

Can a plant-based diet "reverse" heart disease? (2018, April 6). British Heart Foundation. https:/www.bhf.org. uk/informationsupport/heart-matters-magazine/nutrition/ask-the-expert/plant-based-diets

Can gluten cause heart disease? (2020, June 30). Gluten Free Society. https:/www.glutenfreesociety.org/ can-gluten-cause-heart-disease/

Chappell, M. M. (2020, September 10). How to make any recipe vegan (and healthy). Forks Over Knives. https:/www.forksoverknives.com/how-tos/vegan-ingredient-substitutions-swaps-alternatives/

Clean Plates. (2023, August 12). 5 anti-inflammatory snacks that are easy to whip up. Clean Plates. https:/ cleanplates.com/recipes/anti-inflammatory-snacks/

Converting a recipe to gluten-free. (n.d.). The Heritage Cook. https:/theheritagecook.com/converting-recipe-gluten-free/

Crystal, S. (n.d.). The 6 best recipes that won't trigger migraine attacks. With Cove. https:/www.withcove. com/learn/best-migraine-headache-recipes

Davis, J. (2022, February 15). Can plant-based diets help migraine? WebMD. https:/www.webmd.com/ migraines-headaches/plant-based-diets-migraine

Davison, C. (2019, July 8). Diabetes and diet: Here's what you need to know. Forks Over Knives. https:/www. forksoverknives.com/health-topics/vegan-diet-and-diabetes

DeAngelis, D. (2023, August 11). I have chronic inflammation & these are the anti-inflammatory snacks I always have on hand. EatingWell. https:/www.eatingwell.com/article/8064997/anti-inflammatory-snacks-i-always-have-on-hand/

DeAngelis, D. (2023, June 19). 15 Anti-inflammatory snacks for diabetes. Yahoo Life. https:/www.yahoo.com/ lifestyle/15-anti-inflammatory-snacks-diabetes-100000606.html

Deliart Team. (2023, September 12). Gastronomy as an art: The cultural essence of Spanish cuisine. Deliart. https:/www.deliartfoods.com/gastronomy-as-art-cultural-essence-spanish-cuisine/

Dellner, A. (2018, February 15). 15 anti-inflammatory breakfast recipes. PureWow. https:/www.purewow.com/ food/anti-inflammatory-breakfast-recipes

Dirty dozen & clean fifteen. (2022, April 14). Nature's Food Patch. https:/naturesfoodpatch.com/ dirtydozenandcleanfifteen/

Duke, C. (2022, April 23). How to cook with herbs and spices - the definitive guide. To-Table. https:/to-table. com/blogs/recipes/herbs-and-spices-the-definitive-guide

Eating Well Test Kitchen. (n.d.). Tuna salad crackers. EatingWell. https:/www.eatingwell.com/recipe/266426/ tuna-salad-crackers/

Eneojo, O., & Martins, E. (2024). Herbs and spices-based value addition for nutritional and healthy living. IntechOpen. https:/www.intechopen.com/online-first/1177349

Eske, J. (2018, November 20). Coconut milk: Benefits, nutrition, and risks. Medical News Today. https:/www. medicalnewstoday.com/articles/323743

Federal-Ad7989. (2023, May 12). Tips for meal planning & grocery shopping? Reddit. https:/www.reddit. com/r/Cooking/comments/13fogu3/tips_for_meal_planning_grocery_shopping/

Ferchak, D. (2016, March 10). What to eat when you have a migraine, food triggers, and more. Healthline. https:/www.healthline.com/health/migraine/what-to-eat-when-you-have-a-migraine

Fight inflammation with these 20 anti-inflammatory dinner ideas. (n.d.). Allrecipes. https:/www.allrecipes. com/gallery/anti-inflammatory-dinner-recipes/

Fisher, L. (n.d.). 5 anti-inflammatory breakfast options to start your morning. Real Simple. https:/www.realsimple.com/health/nutrition-diet/anti-inflammatory-breakfast

Flavor profiles that pair together in recipes. (n.d.). Nouveau Raw. https:/nouveauraw.com/reference-library/recipe-templates/flavor-prfiles-that-pair-well-in-recipes/

Flynn, J. (n.d.). Can a gluten-free diet relieve joint pain? Arthritis-Health. https://www.arthritis-health.com/blog/can-gluten-free-diet-relieve-joint-pain

Fontesa, Y. (2023, May 29). The art of spice pairing: Unleashing flavorful harmony in your kitchen. Spice Station. https:/spicestationsilverlake.com/the-art-of-spice-pairing-unleashing-flavorful-harmony-in-your-kitchen/

Food in Turkey - Turkish food, Turkish cuisine. (n.d.). Food by Country. http:/www.foodbycountry.com/Spain-to-Zimbabwe-Cumulative-Index/Turkey.html#google_vignette

Goggins, L. (2022, May 19). 24 Anti-inflammatory snacks for a healthy, delicious afternoon. EatingWell. https:/www.eatingwell.com/gallery/7963958/anti-inflammatory-snack-recipes/

Goggins, L. (n.d.-a). 26 anti-inflammatory breakfasts you can make in 15 minutes or less. EatingWell. https:/www.eatingwell.com/gallery/7916792/anti-inflammatory-breakfasts-in-15-minutes/

Goggins, L. (n.d.-b). 34 anti-inflammatory lunches you can pack for work. EatingWell. https:/www.eatingwell.com/anti-inflammatory-lunch-recipes-for-work-7157792

Goggins, L. (n.d.-c). 38 anti-inflammatory dinners you can make in 30 minutes. EatingWell. https:/www.eatingwell.com/gallery/7946056/anti-inflammatory-dinner-recipes-in-30-minutes/

Greens. (n.d.). NutritionFacts.org. https:/nutritionfacts.org/topics/greens/

Grocery Shopping. (n.d.). MyPlate.gov. https:/www.myplate.gov/tip-sheet/grocery-shopping

Guo, X., Wang, H., Xu, J., & Hua, H. (2022). Impacts of vitamin A deficiency on biological rhythms: Insights from the literature. Frontiers in Nutrition, 9. https:/doi.org/10.3389/fnut.2022.886244

Hamilton, C. (2019, January 19). 20 Anti-inflammatory snacks your gut will thank you for. Paleo Blog. https:/blog.paleohacks.com/anti-inflammatory-snacks/

Hamilton, L. (2020, August 1). Should people with diabetes avoid gluten? Diabetes Food Hub. https:/www.diabetesfoodhub.org/articles/should-people-with-diabetes-avoid-gluten.html

Horton, B. (n.d.). 15 Anti-inflammatory breakfast recipes to make mornings a little healthier. LIVESTRONG.com. https:/www.livestrong.com/article/13721857-anti-inflammatory-breakfast-recipes/

How to use herbs and spices in cooking. (2009, June 12). Instructables. https:/www.instructables.com/How-to-use-herbs-and-spices-in-cooking/

Huizen, J. (2021, September 30). Is there a link between gluten and migraine? Medical News Today. https:/www.medicalnewstoday.com/articles/gluten-and-migraine

Hurwitz, K., & Berry, E. (2022, May 8). Heart-Healthy recipes that can be on the table in under 30 minutes. Woman's Day. https:/www.womansday.com/food-recipes/food-drinks/g2176/hearty-healthy-recipes/?slide=8

Jaspan, R. (n.d.). 7 simple meal prep tips. Verywell Fit. https:/www.verywellfit.com/simple-tips-for-healthy-meal-preparation-7556345

JenniferRose. (2015, January 8). Sweet potato and kale balls. Neurotic Mommy. https:/neuroticmommy.com/2015/01/08/sweet-potato-and-kale-balls/

Jibrin, J. (2024, February 6). Best anti-inflammatory foods—plus what to avoid. Forbes Health. https:/www.forbes.com/health/nutrition/best-anti-inflammatory-foods/

Kowalczyk, J. (2022, July). Anti-Inflammatory diet tip: Leafy greens. Sharecare. https:/www.sharecare.com/inflammation/tip-4-greens

Krebs-Holm, L. (2023, June 12). Easy anti-inflammatory weeknight meal recipes. Bezzy Psoriatic Arthritis. https:/www.bezzypsa.com/discover/living-well-psa/health-ask-the-dietitian-easy-anti-inflammatory-weeknight-meal-ideas/

Kubala, J. (2018). The 8 most common food intolerances. Healthline. https:/www.healthline.com/nutrition/common-food-intolerances

Lachtrupp, E. (n.d.-a). Anti-inflammatory diabetes meal plan. EatingWell. https:/www.eatingwell.com/article/7658577/anti-inflammatory-diabetes-meal-plan/

Lachtrupp, E. (n.d.-b). Anti-inflammatory meal plan for healthy blood pressure. EatingWell. https:/www.eatingwell.com/article/7943600/anti-inflammatory-meal-plan-for-healthy-blood-pressure/

Libano. (2022, February 21). An introduction to Lebanese cuisine. Libano. https:/libanorestaurant.com/2022/02/21/an-introduction-to-lebanese-cuisine/

Lin, K. (2020, November 1). Chinese food cultural profile. EthnoMed. https:/ethnomed.org/resource/chinese-food-cultural-profile/

Lynchburg Living. (2024, January 3). DIY spice blends: How to create your own signature seasonings. Lynchburg Living. https:/lynchburgliving.com/diy-spice-blends-how-to-create-your-own-signature-seasonings/#:~:text=Experiment%20with%20proportions%20to%20achieve

MacMillan, A. (n.d.). 13 foods that fight inflammation. Health. https:/www.health.com/mind-body/13-foods-that-fight-inflammation

250 Meade, J. (2016, February 13). An introduction to Mexican food. Moon Travel Guides. https://www.moon.com/travel/food-drink/introduction-to-mexican-food/

Modifying a recipe to be healthier. (2015). Ohio State University. https://ohioline.osu.edu/factsheet/HYG-5543

Nast, C. (2020, April 3). I'm a professional chef and I'm proud to say that I love my Instant Pot. Bon Appétit. https://www.bonappetit.com/story/instant-pot-love-story

Nast, C. (2021, April 1). How to turn nearly any baking recipe into a vegan baking recipe. Bon Appétit. https://www.bonappetit.com/story/veganizing-baking-recipe-tips

Nelson, C. (2021, September 13). How to avoid processed foods: 8 simple tips. GoodRx. https://www.goodrx.com/well-being/diet-nutrition/tips-for-avoiding-processed-foods

No, M. (2024, March 25). 21 anti-inflammatory recipes that are worth trying. Tasty. https://tasty.co/article/michelleno/18-anti-inflammatory-recipes-that-will-make-you-feel-better

Paharia, P. T. (2023, February 28). An overview of the anti-inflammatory effects of nuts. News-Medical. https://www.news-medical.net/news/20230228/An-overview-of-the-anti-inflammatory-effects-of-nuts.aspx

Patiry, M. (2019, June 27). 32 anti-inflammatory breakfast recipes worth waking up to. Paleo Blog. https://blog.paleohacks.com/anti-inflammatory-breakfast-recipes/

Plates, C. (2023, October 3). 7 anti-inflammatory breakfast recipes to feel good all day. Clean Plates. https://cleanplates.com/recipes/anti-inflammatory-breakfast-recipes/

Raman, R. (2017, July 2). How to do an elimination diet and why. Healthline. https://www.healthline.com/nutrition/elimination-diet

Renee, J. (n.d.). Gluten & hypertension. LIVESTRONG.com. https://www.livestrong.com/article/446701-gluten-hypertension/

Rose, N. (2023, July). Can cherries help fight inflammation? PCC Community Markets. https://www.pccmarkets.com/taste/2013-07/nutritionist-cherries

Sanctuary, S. (2012, May 19). Living a life of spices: The art of balancing spices. Living a Life of Spices. http://spicesanctuary.blogspot.com/2012/05/art-of-balancing-spices.html

Shavers, B. (2019, August 5). Heritage Assisted Living. Heritage Assisted Living. https://www.heritageokc.com/blog/vitamin-c-is-best-for-your-sleep-health-want-to-know-why#:~:text=The%20relationship%20between%20sleep%20and%20Vitamin%20C&text=Studies%20have%20shown%20that%20individuals

She Knows Editors. (2018, March 20). Your handy guide to converting any recipe to gluten-free. Taste of Home. https://www.tasteofhome.com/article/converting-recipes-to-gluten-free/

Silver, N. (2021, April 20). Vegan diet for IBS: Research, effectiveness, and tips. Healthline. https:/www. healthline.com/health/irritable-bowel-syndrome/vegan-diet-for-ibs

Simple roasted chickpea snack. (n.d.). Allrecipes. https:/www.allrecipes.com/recipe/197683/simple-roasted-chickpea-snack/

Singmin, C. (2017, September 25). What you need to know about buying and storing bulk foods. Canadian Living. https:/www.canadianliving.com/food/food-tips/article/what-you-need-to-know-about-buying-and-storing-bulk-foods#:~:text=Properly%20store%20your%20goods

Smart shopping 101: How to make a grocery list. (n.d.). Evernote. https:/evernote.com/blog/how-to-make-a-grocery-list

Staples of Thai cuisine. (n.d.). Temple of Thai. https:/www.templeofthai.com/cooking/staple-thai-cuisine.php

10 anti-inflammatory snack recipes. (2021, October 5). Psoriasis Honey. https:/psoriasishoney.org/blogs/post/10-anti-inflammatory-snack-ideas

The Best Vegan Tofu Crumble. (n.d.). Kitchen Stories. https:/www.kitchenstories.com/en/recipes/the-best-vegan-tofu-crumble-8a84

Thomas, D. L. (2023, April 6). What makes blackberries a superfood? News-Medical. https:/www.news-medical.net/news/20230406/What-makes-blackberries-a-superfood.aspx

Tips and techniques for incorporating spices in everyday cooking. (2023, July 12). Johnna Knows Good Food. http:/www.johnnaknowsgoodfood.com

12 types of cuisines around the world. (2022, September 17). Meditation and Family Resort, Kakkadampoyil, Kozhikode (Calicut), Kerala. http:/sattvameditationresort.com/12-types-of-cuisines-around-the-world/2023/07/12/tips-and-techniques-for-incorporating-spices-in-everyday-cooking/

Understanding flavor profiles. (n.d.). The Culinary Pro. https:/www.theculinarypro.com/understanding-flavor-profiles

Upping fruit and veggie consumption to get blood pressure down: What's the case for plant-based diets? (n.d.). McMaster University. https:/www.mcmasteroptimalaging.org/blog/detail/blog/2022/02/03/upping-fruit-and-veggie-consumption-to-get-blood-pressure-down-what-s-the-case-for-plant-based-diets

Using turmeric as anti-inflammatory. (n.d.). UnityPoint Health. https:/www.unitypoint.org/news-and-articles/using-turmeric-as-anti-inflammatory

Wardleigh, C. (n.d.). The health benefits of dark chocolate. SelectHealth. https:/selecthealth.org/blog/2020/09/health-benefits-of-dark-chocolate-selecthealth

252   What Greeks eat. (n.d.). Olive Tomato. https:/www.olivetomato.com/our-greece/

White, A. (2020, August 19). 11 tips for saving money at the grocery store. CNBC. https:/www.cnbc.com/select/how-to-save-on-groceries/

Why eat seasonally? (2019). Seasonal Food Guide. https:/www.seasonalfoodguide.org/why-eat-seasonally

Wicks, L. (2022, April 13). 8 Anti-inflammatory sheet pan dinners with spring produce. Well+Good. https:/www.wellandgood.com/anti-inflammatory-sheet-pan-dinners/

Make a Difference with Your Review

Unlock the Power of Generosity!

"Giving feels good and helps others too." - Someone Wise

People who help others without expecting anything in return often feel happier and live better lives. So, let's try to make a difference together.

I have a question for you...

Would you help someone you've never met, even if you never got credit for it?

Who is this person, you ask? They are like you. They want to be healthier, need some help, and don't know where to start.

My mission is to make anti-inflammatory cooking easy for everyone and to improve overall health. Everything I do is about that mission. And the only way to reach everyone is with *your help*.

Most people decide to read a book based on its cover and its reviews. So here's what I'm asking you to do for a person with inflammation you've never met:

Please help that person by leaving a review for this book.

Your review is free and takes **less than 60 seconds**, but it can change someone's life forever. Your review could help...

...a small business owner serve their community.
...an entrepreneur support their family.
...a person struggling with inflammation and provide the relief they need.
...an unhealthy person to transform their life.
...a dream come true.

To get that 'feel good' feeling and truly help someone, all you have to do is... **leave a review**.

Simply scan the QR code below to leave your review:

scan me to leave a review!

Thank you from the bottom of my heart.

- Your biggest fan, *Albert*

Made in the USA
Coppell, TX
01 December 2024

41477813R00144